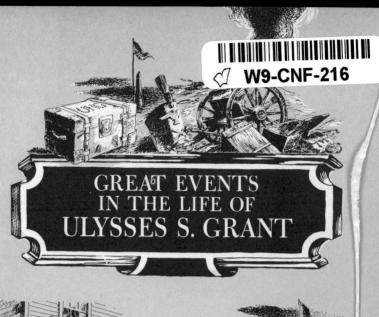

GREAT EVENTS
IN THE LIFE OF
ULYSSES S. GRANT

5 *Resigns from the Army, 1854*

6 *Volunteers in the Union Army at the start of the Civil War, 1861*

8 *Accepts General Lee's surrender of the Confederate Army at Appomattox, Virginia, 1865*

7 *Becomes Lieutenant General of all the Union Armies, 1864*

THE STORY OF
Ulysses S. Grant

"I can't spare Grant. He FIGHTS!"

—ABRAHAM LINCOLN

*With a great, graceful bound, Big York
went over the bar*

THE STORY OF
Ulysses S. Grant

By Jeannette Covert Nolan

Illustrated by Lynd Ward

ENID LAMONTE MEADOWCROFT
Supervising Editor

PUBLISHERS Grosset & Dunlap NEW YORK

PRINTED IN THE UNITED STATES OF AMERICA

Library of Congress Catalog Card No. 52-11070

To

KATHLEEN

Contents

CHAPTER

I Spring Morning   3

II Breaking the Colt   12

III Adventure at the Circus   23

IV Traveling   38

V The Medicine Jug   50

VI "No Very Common Head!"   63

VII Bee in a Bonnet   73

VIII "Step Lively, Mr. Grant!"   81

IX Cadet Days   96

X Soldier in Mexico   103

XI The Torchlight Parade   116

XII "Duty, Honor, Country!"   125

XIII The Western Forts   134

XIV Marching South   144

XV "Never Turn Back!"   152

XVI Joy and Sorrow   167

XVII The New President   176

Illustrations

With a great, graceful bound, Big York
    went over the bar   FRONTISPIECE
"Look, Lyss! Tickets! One for me and
    one for you!"   2
This was the secret mailbox   8
Mr. Grant was sitting on a bench in the
    shed   16
Lady Lou was heading for the gully   42
They coasted on the hillsides   53
"This youth will be President of the
    United States!" he cried   71
"Hundreds of boys want to go to West
    Point," Jake said   74
Before him was a broad parade ground   86
"All right, boys. Let 'er rip!" Ulysses
    cried   113

[*ix*]

ILLUSTRATIONS

"How comfortable we are here," Julia
    often said   119

They went together all over the huge
    camp   148

Mile by mile, the Union regiments ad-
    vanced   159

Grant and Lee shook hands   165

He went to his old home at Galena   173

He stood looking over the sea of up-
    turned faces   179

THE STORY OF
Ulysses S. Grant

"Look, Lyss! Tickets! One for me and one for you!"

CHAPTER ONE

Spring Morning

YOUNG Ulysses Grant felt carefree and happy this morning. It was the first day of vacation in Georgetown, Ohio. The May sunshine was warm and bright. The locust tree bloomed at the gate. Two plump robins were building a nest in the lilac bush.

But where was Dan Ammen?

Ulysses looked up and down the village street. A few wagons and carts rolled by. A few people were strolling toward the square.

"Why is Dan so late when we're going fishing?" Ulysses wondered.

He sat down on the doorstep. The brick house behind him was solid and comfortable. He could hear his mother moving about in-

[*3*]

side, talking quietly to his little sister, Clara. Breakfast was over hours ago, and Mr. Grant had left for the tannery.

"I'm glad that Papa took Simpson with him," Ulysses said to himself. "Dan and I don't want a child of six tagging after us!"

As he waited for his friend, Ulysses took a lump of chalk from his pocket and scribbled on a smooth stone at his feet. He was figuring the number of days until school began again in the fall. He counted the weeks and multiplied by seven.

"It's a good many days," he muttered, "though not enough."

Ulysses had never liked school. He had started when he was five and now he was nine. He had always been promoted because his marks had been above average. He had

[5]

been switched only once with the master's birch rod.

"But I haven't really learned anything in school, except arithmetic and geography," he thought. "I wish Papa would tell me I could quit! But of course he won't! Papa says he believes in education. He says his young'uns have to go clear through the eight grades. What if Papa should send me on to high school and to college?"

Ulysses scribbled rapidly, figuring how many weary days he would have to spend in high school and college. The result was large. It was discouraging!

Surely nobody could believe in that much education!

"No, no," sighed Ulysses, and hastily put the chalk back into his pocket.

Dan Ammen came around the corner of the house. Dan had a fishing pole over his shoulder. With one freckled hand he swung a tin bucket. The other hand was doubled into a fist.

"Hello, Dan," Ulysses said. "Where the dickens have you been?"

"I dug this bucketful of worms," Dan said. "Then Ma made me go on an errand to Pa's newspaper office. The circus man was there. He was asking Pa to write an advertisement for the paper."

"The circus man?" Ulysses repeated.

"He's the agent for the circus," Dan said, opening his fist. "The circus is coming to town next month. And look, Lyss! Tickets! The man gave them to me. One for me and one for you!"

Ulysses stared at the small strips of printed cardboard. "Whoop-ee!" he cried, his blue eyes sparkling. "Circus tickets!"

"Let's hide 'em in our secret mailbox," Dan said.

Ulysses nodded. "Let's do it *now*."

The two boys hurried down the street and into the grove which bordered White Oak Creek. Ulysses drew aside the trailing branches of a giant willow tree on the creek bank. Dan scratched among the willow's roots and lifted out a wooden cigar box.

This was the secret mailbox. Dan opened the hinged lid and dropped in the tickets.

[7]

This was the secret mailbox

"They'll be safe here, Lyss," he said.

"Yes," Ulysses said. "But bury the box, Dan. Bury it deep in the dirt."

As Dan was burying the box, a shrill voice sounded: "U-*lyss*-ees!"

"Who's that?" Dan asked.

"It's Simpson," Ulysses said. "He must have followed us!"

Simpson Grant appeared under the willow tree. He was a stocky, blond little boy in pantaloons.

"What are you doing, Lyss?" Simpson asked. "What's Dan doing?"

"Nothing to bother small fry like you," Ulysses said.

"Papa wants you at the tannery, Lyss."

"Why does he want me? It's my day off."

"He's got a job for you," Simpson announced. "Come on!"

"All right," Ulysses said. "All right."

"I'll go with you and help, Lyss," said Dan.

"Oh, you can't help him," Simpson declared. "Nobody can help."

"Well, I'll go, anyway," Dan said. "It

wouldn't be any fun, fishing all by myself."

The older boys walked briskly, and Simpson skipped after them.

"I don't see why you're so quick to mind your pa, Lyss," Dan remarked. "He never punishes you. He never even scolds you."

"He expects me to mind him," Ulysses said.

"How would he act if you didn't mind him?"

"I don't know," Ulysses replied. "And I don't want to find out."

Simpson chimed in: "Papa was bragging about you to this customer, Lyss. It's Mr. Phipps, from Bethel. Papa told him that you can manage the peskiest horses in the county, and that you haul all the brush and lumber for the tannery fires."

"I wish Papa wasn't always bragging about me," Ulysses said.

"He brags because he's proud of you!" Dan exclaimed.

"And you *are* smart," added Simpson.

"I'm not half so smart as Papa claims,"

Ulysses grumbled. "He tells people things I can do. And then I have to do 'em."

"You don't *have* to, Lyss," Dan said.

"Yes, I do. If I didn't, Papa would be disappointed!"

"Mr. Phipps has a big fine, smoke-colored horse hitched to his wagon," Simpson said, "and a colt tied on behind. Mr. Phipps said the colt's so ornery, nobody can ride him. Papa bet Mr. Phipps fifty cents that you can ride the colt, Lyss. That's the job Papa's got for you."

"It is?" Ulysses grinned and felt happy again. "Shucks, that's no job at all," he said. "I'd rather ride an ornery colt than fish any day!"

CHAPTER TWO

Breaking the Colt

JESSE GRANT'S tannery was near the village square. He had a shop which faced the street. Behind the shop was a wide yard, in which were several brick-walled tanks and a large roofless shed. Here the raw skins of animals, such as pigskin and cowhide, were made into leather.

The process of leathermaking was difficult. The skins had to be scrubbed and scraped, washed and dried. Then they had to be softened with oil and soaked in dyes boiled from the bark of oak trees. But Mr. Grant was a skilled tanner. People in southern Ohio said that his leather was the best to

[*12*]

be had anywhere. Customers came from many other towns to trade with him.

Today, when the boys reached the shop, they saw Mr. Phipps' wagon in the yard.

"There's the bad colt," said Simpson. "His name is Rascal."

The colt was black, with slim legs, and eyes like yellow marbles.

"Rascal's a good name for him," said Dan Ammen. "But Lyss will tame him."

Ulysses was admiring the smoke-colored horse which was hitched to the wagon.

[*13*]

"That one's called Dave," Simpson said. "Isn't he a beauty?"

"Pretty as a picture," said Ulysses, stroking Dave's silky nose. "I wish he was mine."

"You ought to have a horse of your own, Lyss, you're so fond of the critters," Dan said.

"I will, some day."

"Papa and Mr. Phipps are in the shed," said Simpson.

"Well, I'll go in. You two stay out."

Dan winked at Simpson. "Oh-oh! He doesn't want us to hear your pa's tall tales, eh?"

Ulysses did not reply, but what Dan had said was true. He didn't want to be teased about the "tall tales." He loved his father dearly. And he dreaded the thought that anyone should laugh at him for being so talkative and boastful.

Ulysses went slowly into the shed. He hated this place. He hated the smell of the drying skins and the boiling dyes.

"It's an honest, profitable business," Mr. Grant often told him. "Settlers are swarming into Ohio thick as flies. They're pouring over the roads from New England into the new states and western territories. And they all need leather—for shoes, for harness, for dozens of purposes. When I retire, the tannery will be yours and Simpson's."

Ulysses always listened in silence. He would not hurt his father's feelings. But he would never be a tanner.

"Let Simpson have the business," he said to himself. "I'll do something else."

Mr. Grant was sitting on a bench in the shed. With him was a plump, pink-cheeked man in farmer's clothes.

"Ah, here you are, Lyss!" Mr. Grant said heartily. "Mr. Phipps, this is my son, Hiram Ulysses. He'll break your Rascal for you."

Mr. Phipps looked surprised, as he shook hands with Ulysses.

"How-de-do. You're not very big, are you? I thought you'd be big and strong as an ox."

"He *is* strong," Mr. Grant declared. "Yes, sir! A mite short, maybe, but stout, all muscle and nerve. Why, when Lyss was only two

[*15*]

Mr. Grant was sitting on a bench in the shed

years old, he would play in the stall with my
horses. He would crawl between their hoofs
and pull himself up by their manes. The
neighbors were scared. They'd rush in, warn-
ing his mother: 'Hannah, Hannah! The
boy'll be trampled and killed!' "

"And what would his mother say?" inquired Mr. Phipps politely.

"Well, my wife is a calm, quiet woman.
She'd merely say, 'Horses seem to understand
Ulysses—' "

"Papa," Ulysses interrupted, "I'm ready
to ride the colt."

Mr. Grant nodded. "We'll go down to the
square, so you'll have lots of space."

Mr. Phipps had bridled the colt, but he
had been unable to saddle him. Ulysses led
him to the edge of the grass-grown square.
Rascal seemed astonished when Ulysses
leaped quickly on his back. Rascal turned
his head. One yellow eye glared angrily at the
boy. Then he reared on his hind legs and
pawed at the sky. Ulysses dug his bare heels
hard into the colt's flanks. Down thumped

[17]

Rascal's forefeet. He galloped to the opposite side of the square—and stopped.

Ulysses pulled gently on the rein. Rascal flung his forefeet up and snorted.

"Hang on, Lyss!" shouted Mr. Grant. "I bet fifty cents you would. Hang on!"

Ulysses hung on. Rascal lowered his head to the ground and threw his hind legs skyward. He snorted and kicked like a mule. He reared and pitched. But Ulysses had his arms gripped around Rascal's neck. His toes were pressed into Rascal's shoulder blades. Ulysses clung, tight as a burr.

Rascal was furious. He rocked up and down, up and down. Then he tore across the square again. A small crowd had gathered on the pavement. Rascal plunged into the crowd. Everybody yelled and ran. Rascal swerved back into the square.

There he danced in high-stepping circles. His ears twitched. His eyes gleamed wickedly.

Ulysses thought that the colt would finally wear himself out with these crazy antics. And

[*18*]

after a while, Rascal did seem to feel sub-
dued.

He snorted once more and jog-trotted into the street.

Ulysses waved his hand to his father and
Mr. Phipps.

[*19*]

"He's tamed!" Ulysses cried. "I'll ride him a bit, to cool him off—"

But Rascal wasn't tamed. Far from it! He bunched his legs, arched his back, and shot up into the air.

"Like a jack rabbit!" Ulysses thought. "Wow! That's a nasty trick! I'll remember that one!"

Rascal struck out, ripping down the road at top speed.

"You rabbit, you rat—you *rascal!* I'll teach you who's boss!" Ulysses shouted.

Ulysses let the colt run for miles. Then he swung him around and brought him at a decent pace into town.

Mr. Grant and Mr. Phipps were still standing on the pavement.

Ulysses slipped off. He wiped the sweat from his forehead.

"I guess I owe your father fifty cents," Mr. Phipps said.

"Pay it to Lyss," Mr. Grant said, chuckling.

"Thank you, sir." Ulysses took the coin.

"Mr. Phipps, I'd like to buy your horse."

"Buy Rascal?"

"Oh no!" Ulysses grinned. "Rascal's *too* ornery. I'm talking about Dave."

"I'm not anxious to sell Dave," Mr. Phipps said. "My price would be seventeen dollars."

"Will you please not sell him, sir, until I get sixteen dollars and fifty cents more?"

"You seem very earnest, young man. All right," Mr. Phipps said, "it's a bargain."

"What's up your sleeve, Lyss?" asked Mr. Grant.

"Oh, just an idea, Papa," Ulysses answered.

A wonderful idea!

All that day and for many days Ulysses thought of it.

Dave was the finest horse he'd ever seen. He would buy Dave. He would repair an old cart that was rusting in Papa's shed. If he had a mended cart and a horse of his own, he could have a business of his own. A hauling business.

[*21*]

Besides his regular chore of hauling for Papa, he could hire out to other people. He could haul the furniture of families moving from town to town. He could haul kindling, logs, cattle—and travelers on their way.

And his business would be so profitable that Papa wouldn't object to his quitting school. Maybe Papa would not even speak again about his being a tanner.

First, though, Lyss must purchase Dave. How was he to earn the money?

Well, next month the circus was coming. A boy could always find work to do around a circus. And there would be more chances later, chances of all sorts.

"Oh, I'll get the money," he thought, "a little at a time!"

CHAPTER THREE

Adventure at the Circus

A HARD rain fell the day before the circus. During the night rain pattered on the roof. But the morning was hot and clear.

Ulysses wakened at dawn. He dressed quickly and crept downstairs, hoping not to rouse anyone else.

"Good morning, Lyss."

He stared. Yes, there was his mother in the tidy kitchen, putting a pan of bread to bake in the oven. How puzzling, Ulysses thought, that no matter how early he got up, she was always up even earlier! Why, you might imagine that she never slept at all!

"Good morning, Mama."

[23]

Mrs. Grant was brown-haired, smiling, and cheerful. Ulysses thought that she always looked just right in her starched white cap and apron. She wasn't a mother who petted or fussed over her children—but the children always knew that she loved them.

"I won't be home for dinner, ma'am," Ulysses said. "I'll be working at the circus grounds."

"Eat a big breakfast, then," his mother said. "And take some slices of bread and butter with you. What will you do, Lyss?"

"I don't exactly know yet. Dan will be working, too. Are you going to see the show this afternoon?"

"No, I haven't a ticket."

"You can have my ticket," Ulysses said— and drew a breath of relief when she shook her head.

He swallowed his corn-meal mush and gulped down a cup of milk.

"Papa excused me from the chores today," he said, stuffing the paper-wrapped bread and butter into his shirt front. "Good-by, Mama."

"Good-by, Lyss," said Mrs. Grant.

The circus ground was a field not far from the creek. When Ulysses arrived, the field was already humming with activity. Sometime in the night the great red-and-gold wagons had creaked in and unloaded their interesting contents. Three small tents of striped canvas had been raised. Crews of loud-voiced men were unfolding the enormous canvas of the big tent and pounding stakes into the moist earth. At one side were many horses and ponies in a fence-rail pen. Beyond was a row of barred cages in which were chattering monkeys, barking dogs, and other noisy beasts.

Ulysses saw Dan. He was on tiptoe, peeping into one cage after another.

"Look, Lyss!" Dan exclaimed. "Bears and lions—and a rhinoceros!"

"Where are the clowns?" Ulysses asked. "I like them best."

"I reckon any of these men could be clowns —except that one in the stovepipe hat. He's the ringmaster."

"Maybe the ringmaster will give us a job."

[25]

The ringmaster was looking over the horses and ponies. He said that the boys could fetch water for them from the creek.

"Use this tub. And fetch *plenty* of water," he said. "The poor nags are kind o' thirsty."

The tub was light as the boys carried it between them to the creek—but, oh, how heavy as they returned with it! The filled tub really seemed to weigh a ton. And the horses and ponies were *very* thirsty. The boys made trip after trip to the creek. They panted and grunted and groaned. Their feet slipped in the grass, which had been soaked by yesterday's rain.

Once Dan stumbled and sat down—smack!—in the brimming tub. Ulysses had to pry him out again.

At ten o'clock the ringmaster said that the "poor nags" had drunk plenty of water. He paid Dan and Ulysses each a dollar.

"Or would you rather have tickets for the performance?" he asked.

"The money, please," said the boys. "We've got tickets."

The big tent was up now. A man was selling fried fish in a flag-decorated booth. Another man sold sticky popcorn balls. The sun blazed in the sky. There was a lovely smell everywhere of fish, molasses, and damp straw.

[27]

Ulysses and Dan wandered about, feeling rich and gay. At noon they ate Mrs. Grant's bread-and-butter sandwiches. It was almost time for the show to start.

"We'd better fetch our tickets from the mailbox," Ulysses said.

They raced to the creek bank. They unearthed the box—

Rain had seeped in through the lid. The precious tickets were limp, blank strips of cardboard now. All traces of printing were washed away.

"So we won't get to see the circus!" Ulysses said grimly.

"Oh, Lyss! How awful!" Dan moaned. "Well, we can buy tickets."

"Not me!" Ulysses said, thinking of the horse he meant to buy. "I've got something else to do with that dollar."

"Maybe we could explain what happened, to the man at the entrance," Dan said.

It seemed worth trying. They raced back to the field. But the man at the entrance to the big tent would not listen to their explana-

[28]

tion. He looked at the strips of cardboard.

"These ain't tickets," he growled, "and never were."

"Yes, they are!" Dan exclaimed.

"They were," Ulysses said. "They got rained on—"

"Step aside," the man commanded. "You're blocking the way."

The boys stepped aside. People were streaming into the tent—lucky people, with tickets the rain hadn't spoiled. The band commenced to play.

Ulysses put his hands over his ears. He didn't like music. It made his ears ache. The beating of drums made him shiver. He saw Dan dart forward and tug at somebody's coat sleeve. Then Dan tugged at Ulysses' sleeve.

"It's the circus agent, Lyss—"

"What?"

"The man I talked to in Pa's office. He *knows* me!"

The band had stopped for a moment. Ulysses uncovered his ears. He saw that the circus agent was speaking to the ticket collector.

[*29*]

"Let these kids in, Ben," the agent was saying. "I know them. They're not fibbing."

"Yes, sir," said the ticket man. "Well, scoot in, you imps!"

The boys found two vacant seats and squeezed into them. At one end of the tent a

[*30*]

canvas curtain lifted. And with a fanfare, in marched the grand parade:

Jugglers, acrobats, smiling ladies in short, fluffy skirts. Indians in blankets and feathered bonnets. Clowns in baggy white suits, with comical, painted faces!

It was a splendid show. Each act was more exciting than the one before. And last of all, the ringmaster made a speech.

Ulysses and Dan felt that they knew the ringmaster. They felt that he was an old friend.

Now he was saying that there would be an added act—a special treat for the good citizens of Georgetown. They were to see a kangaroo! The ringmaster told them that this animal was rare and unusual. It came from Australia. Few Americans had ever seen it—

"But you, ladies and gentlemen, not only may *see* this freak of nature. You are invited to chase and catch it. Five dollars to the person who catches the kangaroo!"

A wagon was wheeled to the center of the tent.

Out bounded the kangaroo. It stood swaying on its long hind feet. It really was a freak of nature! Everybody roared with laughter.

Several men ran to catch the kangaroo. They ran fast, but the kangaroo was faster. It seemed to have springs in its feet. It dodged

[*32*]

and bounded, always bounding out of reach.

Not one of the men could lay a finger on the kangaroo.

"Time's up, folks," the ringmaster announced. "Too bad nobody won the five dollars. Well, I have five dollars for the person who can ride our dear, sweet little Princess Ida for five minutes!"

A clown led a little pony into the tent. Ulysses had noticed the clown before. He had a monkey perched on his shoulder. He was the funniest of all the clowns. Ulysses had noticed the pony, too. He had carried water to her. She was so fat and sleek that she looked like a small barrel waddling on four thin legs.

"The Princess Ida!" announced the ringmaster. "Who will ride her for just five minutes?"

Dan Ammen got right up out of his seat.

"Lyss will!" Dan cried. "Lyss Grant!"

"I *won't*!" Ulysses said. "Hush, Dan!"

"Oh, go on, Lyss," Dan begged. "That teeny-weeny pony can't be as wild as Mr. Phipps's colt."

Other people in the audience were looking at Ulysses.

"Lyss Grant!" they cried. "Ride her, Lyss!"

Ulysses hesitated. He knew that the pony wasn't as wild as Rascal.

"But she might be tricky," he thought.

"Perhaps Mr. Lyss Grant is frightened," said the ringmaster.

Ulysses wasn't frightened. He went into the ring and took the reins from the clown. He straddled Princess Ida's broad, sleek back— and off the pony trotted, very slowly, around the tent.

"One minute!" the ringmaster said.

Ulysses felt silly. Why, it was just a joke!

"Two minutes . . . Three minutes!"

Princess Ida trotted, slow as a snail.

Suddenly the ringmaster cracked his whip. Princess Ida balked. She jerked and twisted. She bunched her legs and jumped like a jack rabbit.

"Like Rascal," Ulysses muttered. "I know that trick."

"Four minutes!" The ringmaster cracked his whip again.

Princess Ida bolted toward the clown, and the clown grabbed the monkey from his shoulder and tossed it into the air. The monkey landed on Ulysses' head and clutched its furry paws in his hair. Princess Ida streaked on her thin legs the length of the tent—

Ulysses wiggled and squirmed, but the monkey couldn't be dislodged. And Ulysses knew now that this was the prize trick. The ringmaster and the clown had planned it to make people laugh.

And how they were laughing! Ulysses hated the sound of that even more than he hated

[35]

the horrid feeling of the monkey on his head. He gritted his teeth and knew that he would keep on riding Princess Ida—forever, if need be!

The ringmaster fired a pistol in the air. It must have been a signal. Princess Ida stopped

[36]

dead still. The monkey dropped off and was picked up by the clown.

"Hurray for Lyss!" the people shouted. "He did it! Hurray!"

Ulysses' face got very red. This shouting was for him! He was amazed and pleased.

The ringmaster wasn't pleased.

"You ought to be in a circus yourself," the ringmaster said, as he handed Ulysses five silver dollars. "Don't spend it all on candy."

"No, sir," Ulysses said. "I'm going to buy a horse."

CHAPTER FOUR

Traveling

THE next summer Ulysses was ten. He had saved up fifteen dollars with which to buy big, smoke-colored Dave. And he had told his father about the hauling business he hoped to have.

"Well, I suppose you can try hauling," Mr. Grant had said. "But only after school hours and on Saturdays and holidays."

"All right, Papa."

Mr. Grant looked shrewdly at Ulysses. "You don't like school, eh?"

"Not much, sir."

"And you don't like working in the tannery?"

Ulysses wondered how his father had guessed. "Not much, sir."

"I think you may like them both better as time goes on," said Mr. Grant.

Ulysses didn't think so at all, but he wouldn't argue about it. He was more concerned with painting the cart which Papa had given him. It was a stout cart. Mended and painted, it would be as good as new.

One June day Ulysses walked the few miles to Mr. Phipps's house in Bethel and purchased Dave. How proud and independent he felt, as he trotted back toward Georgetown astride his own horse!

During the autumn and winter Ulysses did a great deal of business with his cart. At first he hauled only for short distances, then longer. A hundred and fifty miles to Toledo! Two hundred miles to a town in Indiana! People seemed very willing to trust their property and themselves to him. They said he was a most reliable driver.

"But don't you worry when Lyss goes on these long journeys?" they asked Mr. Grant.

"Oh no," Mr. Grant said. "He's fearless. He can take care of himself."

Mr. Payne, of Georgetown, thought that Ulysses was entirely too fearless. Mr. Payne was riding with Ulysses when the runaway

occurred. They were going to Kentucky, to get an organ which Mr. Payne had bought at an auction sale in Flat Rock. The wagon was

[40]

Mr. Payne's. The horse was his bay mare, Lady Lou.

Mr. Payne said that Lady Lou had been mighty skittish recently.

"She seems to have fits, or something," he said. "I ain't afraid, but I'd just as lief you rassled with her, Lyss."

At the start, Lady Lou was meek as a lamb. Ulysses had driven twenty miles before things became exciting. Then, as the wagon creaked past a cornfield, a vicious-looking, barking dog rushed out.

And Lady Lou promptly had one of her "fits." She began a frantic, zigzag flight which heaved the wagon from side to side, and sent it careening madly on two wheels.

"Slow her down, Lyss!" Mr. Payne shouted.

Ulysses yanked at the lines. He saw that the road curved around a deep gully, and that Lady Lou was heading for the gully. Ulysses strained and yanked at the lines with all his strength.

Just on the brink of the gully, Lady Lou stopped, and the wagon tipped a little to one

[*41*]

Lady Lou was heading for the gully

side. Mr. Payne crawled off the tilted wagon seat.

"Stay in, Mr. Payne," Ulysses said. "She's over her fit now."

"Stay in!" Mr. Payne was pale and shuddering. "Are you plumb daffy? I'll never ride behind that dad-danged hunk o' dynamite again. I'm walking home to Georgetown, and plague take the organ in Flat Rock!"

Ulysses knew that Lady Lou had been terrified by the yapping dog. He patted and soothed her. Then he got into the wagon and drove on to Flat Rock alone.

"That was a runaway!" Mr. Payne said the next day, when Ulysses brought the organ to him. "A real runaway!"

"Yes, it was," Ulysses said. "First one I was ever in."

"You should have turned back, Lyss."

"Oh, I couldn't," Ulysses said.

"You *couldn't?*"

"No, sir. My motto is, 'Never turn back on a road.' "

"Well, by jacks, it ain't my motto," said Mr.

Payne. "I don't hanker to be an angel before my time!"

In the spring Mr. Grant had a letter from his sister, Mrs. Marshall. She lived in Deerfield. She wrote to tell Mr. Grant that her husband had died.

"I wish you could come to see me, Jesse," she wrote.

Of course Mr. Grant decided to go. He said he would travel by steamboat on the Ohio River.

"Would you like to go, too, Lyss?" he asked.

"Yes, *sir!*" exclaimed Ulysses.

The steamer they boarded seemed to Ulysses like a large white swan. He watched Georgetown slip out of sight in the blue mist. Then the boat was gliding between green meadows. The water lapping the sides was bright yellow. But where the great, revolving paddles churned it, the water was foamy white, with spray that sparkled like diamonds.

As they went eastward up the Ohio, Ulysses and his father sat on the sunny deck.

"This is the most beautiful country in the world," said Mr. Grant. "I hope and pray that there will never be a war to destroy it."

"A war, Papa? Why should there ever be a war?"

"Because of slavery," said Mr. Grant. "The

Northern states believe that slavery is wrong and should be abolished. The Southern states see no harm in it. The Southern states claim that if they didn't have Negro slaves, they couldn't raise cotton. And if they didn't raise cotton, the South would be ruined. The quarrel about slavery is an old one, and it's growing more dangerous every year."

"You mean that the North and the South might finally fight each other over slavery, Papa?" Ulysses asked.

"Yes, I think they might. And that would be terrible," said Mr. Grant. "Like brothers fighting!"

"But, Papa, *you* believe that slavery is wrong, don't you?"

"Yes," said Mr. Grant earnestly. "I believe with all my heart that slavery is wrong."

When Ulysses and his father reached Deerfield, Mrs. Marshall hugged them both. Then she burst into tears.

"Now don't you cry, Margaret," said Mr. Grant. "You and your five children are going to live with Hannah and me in Georgetown."

"Oh, no," Mrs. Marshall sobbed. "You haven't room for us all."

"We'll make room," Mr. Grant said. "You know, I'm not a poor man, Margaret. I'll build a wing on our house. Your Jimmy and

our Lyss will be good companions. And your little ones can play with our little ones. Don't you be troubled! I'll tend to everything."

"Jesse Grant, you're the kindest brother anybody ever had," said Mrs. Marshall, smiling through her tears.

The two Grants and the six Marshalls sailed down the Ohio on the grand white steamer. On this voyage Ulysses did not sit talking with his father. He romped around the deck with his young cousins. And when the boat docked for freight at the river towns, he and Jimmy raced up and down the gangplank.

Ulysses showed Jimmy the cabin which they were to share. It was narrow and snug as a closet, with two bunks built into the wall, one above the other.

"You sleep in the upper bunk," Ulysses said. "The lower one is mine."

Jimmy climbed into the upper bunk. "This is the way sailors sleep," he said.

"No, sailors have hammocks," replied Ulysses.

"Well, *soldiers* have bunks," Jimmy declared. "When I'm big, I'll be a soldier."

"I won't," Ulysses said.

"Why not? Don't you want to have a gun?"

"I've got a gun," Ulysses said. "I can beat most everybody in Georgetown, target-shooting. But I don't go hunting. I wouldn't like to kill anything with my gun."

Moonlight was streaming into the cabin,

[48]

through the small, high window. Jimmy gazed down over the side of the bunk at Ulysses. "Is it fun to live in Georgetown?" he asked.

"Oh, yes, lots of fun."

"Why did Uncle Jesse and Aunt Hannah name you Ulysses?"

"Papa got it out of a book."

"I'll bet the fellows call you 'Useless.' "

"Some of them have tried it once," Ulysses said, yawning. "Once, but not twice."

"Why don't they call you Hiram?" asked Jimmy. "That's your first name."

"Well, I wish they would call me Hiram. But they don't," Ulysses said. "And it doesn't matter much."

"If I call you Hiram, will you let me drive Dave sometime?"

"Maybe. Go on to sleep, Jimmy," Ulysses said. And he burrowed under the blanket and began to make loud snoring noises.

CHAPTER FIVE

The Medicine Jug

ULYSSES and Jimmy were always good companions.

They were in the same grade at school. They studied their homework together in the lamplit kitchen. Ulysses showed Jimmy how to solve the hardest arithmetic problems. Jimmy listened while Ulysses practiced the "pieces" he had to recite on Friday afternoons.

"I wish the new schoolmaster had never thought of those dratted recitations!" Ulysses said. "I don't like to get up before everybody and reel off pieces. I feel like sinking right through the floor."

One Friday Ulysses tried to recite Washington's *Farewell Address.* He stuttered and stammered. His knees trembled and his voice was so hoarse that finally the teacher told him to sit down.

Jimmy didn't mind the recitations. He didn't mind the chores at the tannery, either.

He thought that the tannery was a nice, interesting place.

"If you'll do my chores, I'll pay you wages," Ulysses told Jimmy.

"I'll do them," Jimmy replied. "How will you spend the extra time?"

"They're going to build a jail in Georgetown," Ulysses said. "I'm to have the job of hauling the logs."

All winter Ulysses hauled logs for the jail. The weather was cold. Snow lay deep on the hills around the village.

When the last of the logs had been delivered, Ulysses and Jimmy rigged up a sled, using some old lumber they found in the stable. They hitched Dave to the sled and went for long, glorious rides through the snowdrifts. They coasted on the hillsides. They made brush fires, and roasted apples and potatoes in the embers.

Jimmy seldom remembered to call Ulysses by his first name of Hiram. As Ulysses had said, it didn't seem to matter much. And, of course, nobody else called him that.

They coasted on the hillsides

And Ulysses seldom allowed Jimmy to drive Dave—

"Lyss doesn't *look* bossy," Jimmy told Mrs. Marshall. "But he *is*."

The snow melted and White Oak Creek overflowed its banks. The spring weather was cool and blustery. People in Georgetown had the chills-and-fever. And from over in Cincinnati came reports of several cholera cases.

One morning at the breakfast table, Mr. Grant talked about the cholera. It was a dreadful sickness, he said. He hoped and prayed that it wouldn't spread. He didn't want any of his folks catching it!

"I've heard of a man in Maysville, Kentucky, who makes a wonderful medicine," Mr. Grant went on. "One big dose will cure an ailing person, if it's given in time. I'm going to Maysville and buy some of the stuff."

"Buy a large bottle, Jesse," said Mrs. Grant.

"Indeed I will," Mr. Grant said. "Enough for us all, and some to spare to the neighbors."

Simpson looked up from his plate. "Is the medicine nasty, Papa?"

"It's a mixture of drugs and herbs, Sim. It probably doesn't taste good. But the important thing is that it may save a person's life."

Simpson was staring, wide-eyed. "Do people *die* of the cholera?"

"Yes," Mr. Grant said. "Yes, they often do."

Ulysses went with his father to Maysville. Mr. Grant had a new buggy and a team of horses. Ulysses drove the team. The flood water was still high. They forded streams so flooded that the horses had to swim and the muddy water swirled into the buggy.

"Lyss," Mr. Grant said as they crossed one of these streams, "you aiming to drown us?"

Ulysses grinned. "No, sir, just sit tight," he said, and he drove the horses safely across.

They returned that evening. Mr. Grant carried two large jugs into the house. He told Mrs. Grant that the medicine was sold in jugs, not in bottles. He had bought a gallon—

"And the other jug has blackberry cordial in it, Hannah."

"Blackberry cordial!" exclaimed Mrs. Grant. "Whatever for?"

[55]

"I thought we might serve a nip of the cordial to callers at Christmastime," Mr. Grant said. "Put the jugs in the cellar, Lyss."

"And label them, for they're exactly alike," Mrs. Grant added.

"I'll take 'em down cellar for you, Lyss," Jimmy said.

"No, I will," said Simpson.

"Each of you take one," said Ulysses, "while I print the labels."

The cellar was dark when Ulysses went down with the neatly printed labels. The jugs were standing side by side on the shelf. Ulysses pasted the labels on carefully—CHOLERA MIXTURE on one jug, BLACKBERRY CORDIAL on the other.

And then he forgot all about them until a Sunday in July.

That was a very hot day, the hottest of the season. Mr. and Mrs. Grant had gone to a church meeting, taking the younger children with them. Ulysses, Jimmy, and Simpson were playing in the tannery yard with Dan Ammen. The boys had played hare and hounds and follow-the-leader. Now Dan was walking on his hands.

"Look!" Dan said. "Bet you can't do it!"

Ulysses tried—and flopped flat in the weeds and grass.

Jimmy tried—and flopped.

But Simpson walked on his hands for a long time. Then he fell in a heap, flushed and sneezing.

"Kerchoo! *Kerchoo!*" Simpson sneezed violently.

"Sim must be catching something," Dan said.

"I reckon he got dust in his nose," Ulysses said.

"Or maybe he's getting the cholera," said Jimmy.

"The *cholera!*" Simpson sat up and began to wail. "Oh, I'm sick! I've caught the cholera! I'm *dying!*"

Ulysses thought of the medicine jug.

The Grants had kept perfectly well. They hadn't needed the medicine. The jug had never been uncorked.

But Simpson did seem to be ailing now. He was sweating and sneezing. His cheeks were bright scarlet.

"Don't be scared, Sim," Ulysses said. "I know how to cure you."

He pulled Simpson to his feet. With Jimmy and Dan helping, he got Simpson into the house and down into the cellar. Jimmy brought a tin cup from the kitchen. Dan lifted the jug from the shelf.

"What's on the label, Dan?" Ulysses asked.

"It says CHOLERA MIXTURE."

"That's right." Ulysses uncorked the jug. He poured the purple-black liquid into the cup. "Here, Sim. Drink it."

Simpson drank, emptying the cup. Ulysses bent over him.

"How do you feel, Sim?"

"Bad! I feel *bad!*"

"Give him some more," Dan said. "And give me some. I don't feel very good either."

"Give me a swallow," Jimmy said. "I don't feel good at all."

Ulysses filled the cup again for Simpson. He

filled it for Dan and Jimmy. He drank a little of the medicine himself, and was surprised that it should taste so sweet and syrupy.

"Now we needn't be afraid of the cholera," he said.

But Simpson was pressing his hands to his

stomach and wailing: "I've got a pain! An awful pain!"

Ulysses was alarmed. He had thought that Simpson would be better immediately. "Dan," he said, "run for Doc Jones. Jimmy, you help me get Sim upstairs."

Simpson was in bed and Ulysses was pacing the floor when Dan arrived with the doctor.

"Doc Jones is cross as two sticks," Dan whispered. "He *sniffed* at me."

"I don't believe my brother's going to die, sir," Ulysses said anxiously. "I gave him a big dose of the mixture—"

Dr. Jones put on his spectacles. He looked at Simpson and sniffed. He looked at Ulysses and sniffed.

"Young man," he said, "what have you been drinking?"

"The medicine," Ulysses answered. "For cholera. We all had some. But Sim had the most. He had a lot, so I don't think he'll die—"

"Fetch me a sample of that medicine," said Dr. Jones.

Ulysses hastened to fetch a sample. The doctor sniffed.

"Cordial!" he said. "Thick, strong blackberry cordial. No, young man, your brother isn't going to die. He hasn't a single symptom of the cholera. But I don't doubt that he has a stomach-ache. And you tell your pa that my advice is to lick you good!"

The doctor left and Dan went home. Ulysses and Jimmy sat at Simpson's bedside. Ulysses was waiting for his parents to come home from the church meeting. As soon as he saw them in the doorway, he told them what the doctor had said.

"Lick you? I'll do no such thing! Old Doc Jones is a crank," Mr. Grant said. "You meant no harm and you did no harm."

"Sim was more scared than sick," Mrs. Grant remarked. "He just got overheated from the games; and the rich cordial upset his stomach."

"That was my fault, Mama," Ulysses said. "I must have made a mistake, labeling those jugs."

"It could as well be my fault," said Mr. Grant. "I should have had the jugs labeled in Maysville."

"I think maybe it was my fault," Jimmy said. "I don't know which jug I carried down to the cellar."

"Or mine," Simpson added. "I never did know whch jug was which."

"Don't you blame yourself, Lyss," said Mr. Grant.

"No, don't." Mrs. Grant smiled, as she arranged Simpson's pillows. "By tomorrow our invalid will be chipper as a squirrel."

Ulysses smiled, too, and blinked his eyes.

Surely no other boy had ever been blessed with a family so loyal and understanding!

CHAPTER SIX

"No Very Common Head!"

L YSS," said Simpson, "what's a *phrenologist?*"

The two boys were in the stable. Ulysses had been grooming and currying Dave. He paused a moment and sat down on the harness chest to think about Simpson's question.

"A phrenologist," he said, "is a man who rubs the bumps on your head and then tells you what kind of a person you are."

"Bumps?" Simpson repeated. "I haven't any bumps on my head!"

"Yes, you have," Ulysses said. "Everybody has. And a phrenologist claims that each bump tells something about your character."

"My character? What's that, Lyss?"

"It's—well, it's *you*. Your disposition, the goodness or badness that's in you, and the things you can or can't do."

"Like my soul?" Simpson said.

"Yes, I suppose so. What made you think of a phrenologist, Sim?"

Simpson pulled a crumpled paper from his

pocket. He straightened the paper. "I was down at the square this morning. A man was tacking these announcements on the fences and stores. He gave me one. Look! Read it!"

Ulysses read aloud: " 'Professor Franconi, World-Famous Phrenologist, will be seen and heard in a Public Lecture at the Georgetown Schoolhouse, November 7, 1835. 8:00 P.M. A Stupendous Spectacle! Come One, Come All!' "

"November seventh is next Saturday," Simpson said. "It was Professor Franconi himself, tacking up the papers. He wears earrings, like a gypsy. Are you going to the lecture, Lyss?"

"I wouldn't miss it," Ulysses said. "The whole town will turn out for it, probably."

During that week there was much talk of the "Stupendous Spectacle" in Georgetown.

Some people believed that phrenologists were very wise. Other people said that they were no wiser than gypsy fortunetellers. But, as Ulysses had expected, the whole town attended Professor Franconi's lecture. At eight o'clock on Saturday night the schoolhouse was packed to the doors.

Ulysses, Simpson, and Jimmy had gone early, with Dan Ammen. They sat in the front row. There were twelve boys in the row. By craning his neck, Ulysses could see his father. Mr. Grant had been unable to find a seat. He was standing in the aisle with Dan's father and several other men.

On the platform behind the schoolteacher's desk were two chairs. One chair was occupied by Mr. Buckner, the proprietor of Georgetown's hardware store. Mr. Buckner was big and gruff and unpopular with his neighbors.

"What's Mr. Buckner doing up there?" Ulysses asked Dan.

"He got the Professor to speak here tonight," Dan said. "Mr. Buckner knows him."

Just then Professor Franconi appeared on the platform. He had a thin, white face and long black hair which curled on the velvet collar of his long black coat. His earrings were loops of gold. His necktie was a white silk scarf. His hands were long and white, and he waved them in graceful gestures as he began to lecture.

Professor Franconi described the human head. The average person, he said, might think that all heads are alike—and as smooth as eggs—

"But no, my friends! All heads are different in shape and size. And they are not smooth. They are masses of bumps and hollows. I am a great phrenologist. I can lay my fingers lightly on a head and find these bumps and hollows. And when I have done so, I know almost everything about the owner of the head. I shall demonstrate!"

Professor Franconi bowed to Mr. Buckner. He laid his fingers on Mr. Buckner's head.

"This gentleman," he said, "is a successful merchant. He is good-humored and charitable. Georgetown loves him!"

Mr. Buckner smiled and looked pleased. He bowed to the Professor.

Some people clapped, and a few laughed.

"Perhaps you imagine that I am right about Mr. Buckner only because he is an acquaintance of mine," the Professor said. "I shall examine more heads. Young heads! You boys in the front row, step forward. Come and line up before me. I'll tell you what you are—and what you will be in the future."

The boys laughed and nudged one another. They got slowly to their feet and went up to stand in a straggling line before Professor Franconi.

Ulysses was at the end of the line. He saw those long white hands fluttering over the first boy's head.

"I feel foolish," he thought; and he wished that he had remained in his seat.

The first boy's name was Johnny Watkins.

"You like to argue," said the Professor to Johnny. "You'll be a lawyer."

The second boy was Seth Smith.

"You have a large bump of thrift. Some day you'll be a banker," said the Professor.

The third and fourth boys would be farmers, the Professor predicted, as he moved down the line. Dan Ammen would be a preacher, and Jimmy Marshall a soldier.

"A-ha!" exclaimed Jimmy, winking at Ulysses.

The Professor was moving rapidly. He

touched Simpson's head. "You will be—the pilot of a steamboat," he said.

"Oh, *good!*" breathed Simpson.

Then the Professor was rubbing Ulysses' head. He rubbed and rubbed. It seemed that he would never stop. Ulysses grew red and embarrassed.

"It's worse than the time at the circus, when I rode Princess Ida," Ulysses thought. "It's even worse than Washington's *Farewell Address.*"

Suddenly the Professor said: "This is no very common head, my friends. This is an *extra-ordinary* head! The owner of this head has a most unusual future."

Ulysses looked back at his father. Mr. Grant's face was serious. He was listening to every word.

"You are stubborn," the Professor said to Ulysses. "Aren't you?"

"Well, maybe I am, sir," Ulysses murmured, "at times."

"But you're truthful. You always tell the truth, don't you?"

"I—I try to, sir."

[*69*]

The Professor rubbed again. "You are quick at figures. Mathematics is your best study. You're patient, not often angry. And you're smart—at least, you have sense enough to come in out of the rain."

Somebody laughed; and Ulysses saw that his father was frowning.

"You will *not* be a doctor—"

Now, nearly everybody laughed, for the story of Simpson's stomach-ache was known in the village.

The Professor snatched the white scarf from his eyes and gazed at the audience.

"This youth will be *President of the United States!*" he cried.

Then he bowed low, his long black hair dangling and his earrings bobbing. The lecture was finished.

Ulysses ducked out the side door and waited in the shadows for Simpson, Jimmy, and Dan. He could hear the audience still laughing. He heard Johnny Watkins' father shout: "Oh, don't be so swelled up, Jesse. The Professor says that about every boy." And he heard Pa-

*"This youth will be President of the
United States!" he cried*

pa's voice, replying: "But he didn't say it about *your* boy, eh, Watkins?"

"Papa believes it," Ulysses thought. "I wish he wouldn't!"

Ulysses was late getting home. His father was in the parlor, reading a newspaper.

"Papa," Ulysses said. "Dan and I were talking about Professor Franconi. We think he does the same stunt wherever he lectures. He picks out some boy or other and says the boy will be President."

Mr. Grant looked up. "I don't think so. Anyway, why should you have been the boy he picked?"

"Mr. Buckner might have told him how you're always bragging about me."

"Bragging? I don't brag! Never! If I sometimes remark to folks that you're the cleverest boy in town, that's not bragging. Because you are!"

"But, Papa, I'm not going to be President of the United States!"

Mr. Grant rattled his newspaper. "I guess it could happen, Lyss," he said.

CHAPTER SEVEN

Bee in a Bonnet

THE summer that Ulysses was fifteen, Lieutenant Jake Ammen visited in Georgetown.

Jake Ammen was Dan's older brother. He had been educated at West Point, the United States Military Academy in New York. Now he was a teacher there.

One evening Jake and Dan came to call on the Grants. Jake told them all about West Point. He said that it was a fine and famous school. Ever since Revolutionary War days, it had trained young men to be officers in the United States Army.

"Hundreds of boys want to go to West Point," Jake said. "But the school is small and only a certain number can be admitted. The

"Hundreds of boys want to go to West Point," Jake said

Congressmen in Washington decide which boys can go. I had hoped that Dan could have the next appointment. But it's already been promised to Bart Bailey. So my father got Dan an appointment to the United States Naval Academy at Annapolis, Maryland, instead."

"Bart Bailey is just Lyss's age," Mr. Grant said. "Is he old enough for West Point, Jake?"

"No, sir, not yet," Jake answered. "Bart will have to wait two years before he can take the entrance examinations. It's a very stiff exam. If Bart shouldn't pass it, our Congressman would have to appoint some other Georgetown boy. What are your plans for Lyss, Mr. Grant?"

"Well, Lyss is through with school here," Mr. Grant said, looking thoughtful. "In the fall he's going to the Presbyterian Academy in Ripley. After a year or two at Ripley, I'll send him to college somewhere."

Mrs. Grant was sitting in the rocking chair, holding Orvil, her newest baby, in her lap. "Lyss," she said, "I baked a batch of ginger cookies today. Will you fetch a plate of them from the kitchen?"

"Yes, Mama."

Ulysses got up quickly, for he never really enjoyed conversations about schools and studying. He went into the kitchen, and Dan followed him.

"Do you want to go to Annapolis, Dan?" Ulysses asked.

"Oh, sure," Dan replied. "I'd rather it was West Point, because Jake's there. But the Navy suits me fine."

"Remember when Professor Franconi said you'd be a preacher?"

Dan laughed. "Imagine me a preacher! That Professor Franconi was a humbug. He was a windbag."

"He was talking through his hat," Ulysses said. "Imagine me being President!"

Dan ate several cookies in an absent-minded way. "What *will* you do, Lyss?"

"Oh, Papa always has some bee in his bonnet, and now it's Ripley," Ulysses said. "I'll go, to please him. After that, I'll have my hauling business, and people will hire me for driving jobs."

"But you can't haul and drive your whole life long!" protested Dan. "Golly, your pa would be mad as a wet hen, if you did!"

Ulysses sighed. "Well, I won't fret about it for a while. I won't make a lot of plans. I hate planning things. It's much better, I think, just to do them, if you have to. Hey, Dan, let's take these cookies into the parlor before you eat them *all*."

When Dan and Jake had left, Ulysses and Simpson went up to their bedroom. Simpson was sleepy and climbed right into bed. Ulysses undressed more slowly. As he was pulling off his shoes, Mr. Grant came in.

"Lyss," Mr. Grant said, "how would you like to go to West Point?"

Ulysses didn't say anything. He pulled off his socks and stuffed them into his shoes.

"A wonderful place!" Mr. Grant exclaimed. "And wouldn't you like to be commissioned as an officer in the United States Army?"

Ulysses pulled his nightshirt over his head, still without saying anything. He felt that he

[*77*]

wouldn't like West Point one bit. It was probably a place where the rules were strict, where bugles tootled and drums banged from dawn to dark. As for being an army officer—oh, no! Never!

But he was sure that his father would soon forget about West Point. And he wanted to please him. So at last he said: "I would go, Papa, if I had the chance."

Then Ulysses jumped into bed, Mr. Grant went out of the room, and Simpson sat up, grinning.

"Lyss, will your uniform have gold buttons, the same as Jake's?" Simpson whispered.

"My uniform?"

"While you and Dan were in the kitchen, Papa told Jake that he means to write to our Congressman about you," Simpson said. "Papa and Jake both think that Bart Bailey might not pass the exam. I'll bet you get that appointment yet!"

"No," Ulysses said. "Bart will pass the exam all right. Anyway, it's two years off. I've made up my mind not to worry!"

In the fall Ulysses went to Ripley, and he did not worry. But how quickly the months whisked by! In the Christmas holidays of the second year, his father handed him the letter from the Congressman.

"You've been appointed to the United States Military Academy, Lyss," he said.

[79]

Ulysses read the letter. The Congressman had written that Bart Bailey of Georgetown had failed the entrance examination for West Point. Jesse Grant's son, Ulysses, had been appointed in his place.

Ulysses was stunned. "But, Papa, I don't want to go!" he cried.

"You said you did!" his father exclaimed. "You gave me your word."

"Yes, sir, because I never dreamed that Bart would fail."

For once Mr. Grant's face was stern. "I took you at your word, Lyss. I asked for the appointment. Here it is. And I think you *will* go. You will finish this term at Ripley and go to West Point not later than the fifteenth of next May."

"Yes, sir," Ulysses said unhappily. "I'll go, of course. I'll keep my word."

CHAPTER EIGHT

"Step Lively, Mr. Grant!"

THE railroad train was skimming through the May landscape at the terrific speed of twelve miles an hour!

Ulysses peered out the window. He could scarcely believe that he was really on his way to West Point. This was his first ride in the new-fangled steam cars, and he had been secretly hoping for an accident of some sort. Nothing serious, of course. No, just a small accident, which would be a good reason for not going farther.

The train might be wrecked. The engine might collide with another engine. The string of cars might slide off the iron rails.

"I wouldn't mind being hurt a little," he thought. "Suppose I lost a finger or a couple of toes? I could spare them. And any boy with

missing fingers or toes would be sent home from West Point immediately!"

Ulysses waited and hoped for the accident. But the train sped on in clouds of smoke and cinders, and at last puffed into the station at New York City.

A pretty white steamboat took Lyss up the Hudson River to West Point. He stood at the rail of the boat, with his small trunk beside him. Jimmy Marshall had hammered brass tacks into the lid of the trunk. The tacks formed initials: *U. H. G.*

"You're Hiram Ulysses Grant," Jimmy had said. "But if we put the tacks in *H. U. G.,* that spells *Hug,* and people might laugh at you. So why not switch them around?"

Ulysses had agreed to this. Now he was very glad that Jimmy had made the change. It would be awful if he were called *Hug!* He felt like a country jake, anyway, in his wide straw hat, plaid coat, and wide pantaloons.

The boat went upstream between high, chalky bluffs and docked at the West Point pier. Ulysses alighted and hoisted his trunk to his shoulders. A steep wooden staircase rose from the pier to the edge of the bluff above.

[*83*]

Ulysses toiled up the staircase to the top, and paused.

Before him was a broad parade ground. Young men in gray uniforms were marching

along neat gravel paths which led to the old buildings of brick and stone. Ulysses saw rows of cannon and a large, low-roofed stable. He saw a post with a placard nailed to it. *"Register at the Adjutant's office,"* said the placard.

Ulysses found the Adjutant's office. A man was sitting at a desk inside. The man glanced up.

"Your name, please?" he said.

Ulysses thought of those brass tacks. "Ulysses Hiram Grant," he replied.

The man frowned. "That name is not on our list," he said. "I have the name of Ulysses S. Grant, of Ohio."

"That's it. That's me."

"But if your middle name is Hiram, you should be listed as Ulysses *H.* Grant."

"I guess our Congressman got mixed up," Ulysses said. "Just change the middle initial to *H.*"

"Oh no," the man said. "Your Congressman appointed Ulysses *S.* Grant to the Academy. If you're that person, you may sign the register. If not, you have no appointment and you can clear out."

Ulysses was thinking swiftly. He had never

Before him was a broad parade ground

wanted to come to West Point. And here was a good excuse for going home. He had only to insist that his middle initial was *H.*, not *S.* Then he could "clear out."

But he remembered his motto, "Never turn back on a road." He remembered that he had given Papa his word.

"Sir," he said, "I am Ulysses S. Grant of Ohio."

"Very well," the man said. "Sign *U. S. Grant* in the register."

As Ulysses was writing, three tall gray-clad cadets came into the office. They were upper-classmen. They looked at Ulysses' signature.

"U. S. Grant!" cried one of the cadets. "Hi, greenhorn! So you're United States Grant, eh? Little old Uncle Sam! Hello, Sammy!"

Sam Grant was the name by which Ulysses would be known all through his years at West Point.

Ulysses spent that first night in a small room in the great stone barracks. His roommate was George Derby. The boys were tired. They lay down on their cots. They were dozing off, when the door burst open and a young man wearing an officer's uniform strode in.

"Get up, you beasts!" he commanded. "Salute!"

The boys saluted.

The young man thrust a book at them. "Memorize twenty pages of this book to recite tomorrow morning!"

The door slammed. Ulysses put the book on a chair and got back into bed.

"You'd better start memorizing," George Derby said.

"That wasn't an officer," Ulysses said. "No officer would call us beasts. It's a joke. Jake Ammen told me to watch out for such jokes."

"Who's Jake Ammen?" asked George.

"A friend of mine," Ulysses said. "Jake was a student here, and then a teacher. He has resigned from the Army now. That's what I'm going to do. I'll be a soldier for a few years, but not forever."

George grinned. "You think you weren't cut out for this job?"

"I *know* I wasn't," Ulysses said. "I want a

quiet, peaceful life. But while I'm on the job, I intend to make good at it."

Ulysses would never forget his first month at West Point. He could not take his entrance examination until July. Therefore, in June he was not even a "plebe" cadet. He was just called a "Thing." And with the other "Things," he had to learn the ways of the cadet corps.

He had to learn to march, to drill, and to obey orders.

He was awkward at marching, for the drums bothered him. Oh, those awful drums! He was drummed awake in the morning. He was drummed to roll call, to inspection, to classes, and to the sunset parade. In the evenings he studied for the coming exam. And at ten o'clock he was drummed to bed.

Cadet officers were in charge of the "Things." These upperclassmen seemed never to stop shouting commands:

"Step lively, *Mister* Grant! Stand straight! Salute! Throw out your chest, shut your trap, pick up your clumsy feet! Can't you hear the drum, *Mister* Grant? You're a peach of an Uncle Sam! You're a beast! You're an ani-*mule!*"

As Examination Day approached, Ulysses was nervous.

"Papa would be terribly sad if I failed," he thought. "I mustn't fail!"

He studied very hard and passed the examination. Soon he was writing a joyful letter to his father:

"I am a *plebe* now. I can get my uniform. A swallow-tailed gray coat with a high, quilted collar. A gigtop cap. White pants which fit as tight to the skin as the bark fits to a tree. If I bend over quickly or run, they're likely to crack with a report as loud as a pistol."

Ulysses was not homesick at West Point. For a while everything seemed strange and confusing to him. But before the year was out, he had become interested in his work and contented. He liked the beautiful views from his windows. He liked the morning and evening ceremony of raising and lowering the flag.

The motto of the Academy was "Duty, Honor, Country."

"I like that," Ulysses thought. "It can be mine. I'll have two mottoes and remember them both."

Ulysses made many friends at school. His classmates knew him to be steadfast, dependable, and truthful. During his second term, Rufus Ingalls was his roommate.

"Sam Grant is a rock," Rufus Ingalls often said. "A regular old *rock*. When everybody else flies off the handle, Sam Grant is cool as a cucumber. When he tells you something, you can *believe* it. And he's no sissy. No, indeed! He's always ready for a lark."

Rufus himself was a fun-loving boy. One afternoon Rufus came into the room where Ulysses was studying. Rufus was smiling mysteriously.

"What are you thinking about, Rufe?" Ulysses asked, looking up from his book.

"Turkey," Rufe said. "Roast turkey and mince pie."

"Is that what we're having for supper?"

"Oh, no," Rufe said. "Bully beef for supper. Turkey and mince pie at midnight. Want some, Sam?"

"I certainly do. A large helping, please."

"I knew you would. Listen!" Rufe said. "Derby went for a walk today. He bought the turkey and the pie from a farmer. He's having a feast at midnight. Only a few of us are invited. Will you come?"

"Of course I will!" Ulysses exclaimed.

"Even though it's against rules?"

Ulysses snapped his fingers. "Some rules are made to be broken," he said.

At midnight Rufus and Ulysses crept along the dark hall to Derby's door. They rapped three times. The door opened and a wonderful smell wafted out.

"Hey, Rufe," Ulysses whispered, "Lieutenant Grier is on guard duty. If he gets a whiff of that turkey, the jig is up!"

The boys went in and shut the door. The room was dimly lighted by the red coals in the fireplace. Three other boys sat on the floor. Derby and his roommate, Deshon, knelt on the hearth, turning the turkey on a spit.

"What a magnificent bird!" Rufus exclaimed. "How plump and juicy!"

"I smuggled in some root beer," said Deshon.

"Good old Deshon!" murmured Ulysses. "What a spread!"

At that moment boots tapped in the hall.

Instantly the turkey, the mince pie, the

root-beer bottles were swept under the cots.
Derby and Deshon leaped to their feet. The

other boys flattened themselves on their stom-
achs in the room's shadowy corners.

The door swung open and Lieutenant

Grier glanced in. Derby and Deshon were standing together, their backs to the fireplace. They clicked heels and saluted.

Lieutenant Grier stared silently at Derby and Deshon. Then he slowly closed the door and his boots were heard tapping as he walked on down the hall.

Out came the food. Derby sliced the turkey. Deshon uncorked the root beer. Rufus divided the pie.

"A narrow squeak, men!" said Derby, laughing.

Rufus lifted his bottle of root beer. "Here's to the good old rules that were made to be broken."

"And here's to good old Grier, who seems to have no sense of smell," said Ulysses.

CHAPTER NINE

Cadet Days

ULYSSES GRANT was not the most brilliant member of his class at West Point. He studied just enough to make average grades in the tests which were held every six months. He sometimes got the "black marks," or demerits, which were given for not having his shoes properly tied, his buttons polished, or his room clean and neat. But there was one thing which he could do better than anybody else.

He rode splendidly. He was the champion horseman of the Academy. Sergeant Herschberger, the riding master, even allowed him to ride Big York. This long-legged sorrel was the most spirited horse in the Academy's stables.

"He's a jumper," Sergeant Herschberger said. "He's got a nasty temper and he's full of beans and business. We've never had anyone here, until Cadet Grant came, who could ride Big York. But he can do it. Cadet Grant is a

wizard with dumb critters. I hope I'll have the opportunity to show him off before he leaves the school."

In his Senior year, Ulysses had Fred Dent of St. Louis as his roommate. Frank Gardner was his neighbor across the hall.

Gardner was a mischievous fellow. He played many tricks on his friends. And he was planning to play one on Ulysses.

"Have you noticed how calm Sam Grant is?" Gardner said one evening to Fred Dent. "Too calm. He never gets rattled, does he? Well, I'm going to rattle Sammy."

"How will you do it?" Fred asked.

Gardner winked. "Wait a bit. You'll see."

Next day as the cadets were marching into the classroom for a lesson in mathematics, Gardner suddenly handed Ulysses a huge gold watch.

"Look, Sam," he said. "Look at my new watch."

Ulysses was holding the watch when the professor ordered the class to be seated. He tried to give it back to Gardner, but Gardner had turned away. Hastily Ulysses crammed the watch into a pocket inside his coat and buttoned it down.

This was Ulysses' day to write a problem on the blackboard. Soon the professor ordered him to rise.

"Solve your problem and explain it aloud and in detail," said the professor.

"Yes, sir," Ulysses replied, getting up.

The watch was ticking noisily against his chest. He hoped the professor wouldn't hear it!

Ulysses wrote his problem on the board. He had just begun to explain it when a great *bong-bong-bong* sounded in the room.

The professor raised his head. "Where's that ringing coming from?" he demanded.

Ulysses knew where the ringing came from. It was loud and strong under his coat. *Bong-bong-bong!* But Ulysses did not flinch. He went on reciting in a calm, clear voice. And as he sat down again, the ringing stopped.

"A good recitation, Mr. Grant," said the professor, nodding. "I congratulate you on being able to speak above the din. I wonder what caused it. Now let us continue with the lesson."

By this time everybody except the professor realized that Gardner had been up to one of his tricks. The cadets were all grinning. After class they crowded around Ulysses, laughing and thumping him on the back.

Ulysses laughed, too. "Your watch has an alarm in it, Frank," he said. "You knew I would have to write on the board. You wound and set the alarm so it would ring just when I was reciting."

"I wanted to rattle you, Sam," Gardner said. "But you outsmarted me, old boy."

"Old steady Sam Grant," said Fred Dent admiringly. *"Nothing* rattles him!"

In June, 1843, thirty-nine young officers were graduated from West Point. Hundreds of people came from far and near to attend the graduating exercises and to see the cadets display their horsemanship. The riding hall was thronged.

The mounted cadets paraded and wheeled. They flashed their swords and put their horses over the bars. Then they formed in a long line down the center of the hall, as if for some important event.

Sergeant Herschberger walked out to the jumping bar. He lifted it very high, higher than his head, and fixed it in place.

"Cadet Grant!" the sergeant shouted.

Ulysses galloped from the line. He was riding Big York. He galloped to the end of the hall. He turned and galloped toward the bar. Big York's hoofs thudded faster, faster. With a great, graceful bound, Big York went over the bar.

There was a moment's hush. Then Sergeant Herschberger shouted: "Cadet Grant's jump of more than six feet is a record for the Academy. Very well done, Cadet Grant!"

Later Ulysses and Fred Dent were in their room, packing their trunks. They had been commissioned as second lieutenants of infantry. Fred was going to an army post in the South. Ulysses was to be stationed at Jefferson Barracks in Missouri.

"Why, that's just outside St. Louis," Fred

[*101*]

said. "You must call on my parents. You'll be only a few miles from our house, Sam."

"Thanks, Fred, I will call on your parents," Ulysses said. "It will be mighty nice to have some friends in Missouri."

CHAPTER TEN

Soldier in Mexico

ONE hot summer night Lieutenant Ulysses S. Grant sat inside an army field tent, writing a letter.

He had taken off his big floppy white cap and the blue coat of his uniform. He had stuck a lighted candle into the neck of a bottle and placed the bottle on an upturned box. Through the open door of the tent, he could see the flicker of candlelight in hundreds of other tents. He could see the flame of many campfires and the black hump of a distant mountain range.

At the top of his letter Ulysses had written: *Mexico, June 12, 1846.*

He looked at the date and thought of the three years which had passed since his graduation from West Point. He thought of the months he had spent at Jefferson Barracks in Missouri. He remembered how he had gone to call on Fred Dent's family. At the Dents' house, he had met Fred's pretty sister, Julia.

Ulysses had fallen in love with Julia Dent. He had wanted to marry her right away. But just then war had been declared between the United States and Mexico, and Ulysses' regiment was ordered to the front.

Now he was writing a letter to Julia, telling her about the war.

The two countries were fighting over a narrow strip of land which stretched from the Neuces River to the Rio Grande. The Mexicans claimed this land as theirs. The United States insisted that it was a part of the new State of Texas.

"We are winning the battles," Ulysses wrote. "We have better soldiers, better equipment, and more guns than the Mexicans. But what is this strip of land really worth? Surely it's not worth the lives which will be sacrificed here."

As Ulysses' pen scratched rapidly, someone came into the tent.

"Hello, Sam!"

Ulysses looked up and saw his old comrade, Fred Dent. "Fred!" he exclaimed joyfully. "I didn't know you were in camp!"

"I arrived today," Fred said. "I ran across several of our West Point friends at headquarters. They told me where to find you. But what's that stubble on your chin, Sam? By Jove, you're growing a beard! And it'll be red!"

"Wrong!" said Ulysses, laughing. "It's

brown. Sit down and talk to me. I was just writing to Julia. I suppose you've heard that I'm going to marry your sister as soon as the war's over?"

"Oh, yes," Fred said. "Julia told me."

They talked of their experiences in the war. Ulysses said that he hated war and would always hate it.

"The battles don't scare me," he said. "But I hate this climate, and the long marches through desert sand and glaring sun. And I hate taking care of the mules."

"Mules?" Fred repeated in surprise.

"I've been made quartermaster of the regiment," Ulysses said. "In a little while the Army will march to Monterrey. Lucky fellows like you will be commanding the troops. I'll be trailing behind with a supply outfit, commanding a bunch of pesky mules."

Fred whistled. "I don't envy you that job. I guess word must have got around that you're a 'wizard with dumb critters.'"

"I guess so," Ulysses said, sighing.

After an hour of conversation, Fred went

off to his own tent. It was months before the two friends met again.

Ulysses was very busy, hiring mules from Mexican peasants and organizing his supply train. The Army started for the Mexican city of Monterrey. Each morning the mules were loaded with their heavy burdens of tent poles, canvas, kettles, and packs of foodstuffs. Then they set out. All day the procession followed the troops. Each evening, at a new campsite, everything was unloaded once more. Ulysses worked hard. He did not complain.

"But I can't say that I enjoy my job!" he thought.

At last the army reached Monterrey. The city was fortified by stone walls and by Mexican cannon in the surrounding hills. Ulysses saw the American regiments massing for the attack. He knew that he was expected to remain behind the lines with his supply outfit. But when the battle began, he jumped on his horse and rode forward.

The Americans were charging. They were trying to batter their way through those stone walls. Ulysses saw a section of one wall crumble and go down. He went closer and saw the Americans pouring into the streets of the city.

Then, somehow, Ulysses found himself among the troops, riding at the head of a column of soldiers.

"Charge, men! *Charge!*" he cried.

The Americans advanced, firing their guns. Then they seemed to falter. They were running out of ammunition! A distressed and sweating colonel shouted that they would have to get ammunition from another regiment somehow.

"Who will volunteer to go across the city

and bring us ammunition?" the colonel shouted.

"I'll go!" Ulysses said, and he spurred his horse to a wild gallop.

The streets of Monterrey were full of Mexicans. At every corner their shells were bursting. Through the showers of bullets Ulysses galloped. Up and over the walls he went, crossing the city.

In a short time he was galloping back with three great sacks of ammunition. The colonel snatched the sacks and distributed the ammunition. The Americans began firing again. No one thanked Lieutenant Grant. No one even mentioned his daring ride. But when the Americans captured Monterrey, Ulysses felt that perhaps he had helped a little in the victory.

The Mexicans were being defeated everywhere. They retreated to Mexico City. This was their national capital. Mexico City was guarded by rocky hills and all the hills were bristling with fortresses.

General Winfield Scott, the commander in chief of the United States Army, planned to capture these fortresses, one at a time. Then he could take the capital.

Ulysses' regiment was with the troops which General Scott led. The struggle for Mexico City was long and bitter. Days and weeks dragged by. Ulysses was still serving as the quartermaster, but he was often in the midst of the fighting.

One morning Ulysses and some of his men got lost from the regiment. They were trapped in a churchyard in a Mexican village. Around them were flat-roofed houses. On the roofs, crouched behind the chimneys, were dozens of Mexican snipers. Ulysses and his men were towing a small cannon. But the cannon was of no use to them, because their enemies were so high above their heads.

"We must get the cannon up on a level with those roofs," Ulysses said. "We must make a clean sweep of the roofs, before the Mexicans pick us off, one at a time. Look, boys! See the bell tower on that church? We'll take the cannon to pieces and hoist the pieces up into the tower."

The men quickly took the cannon apart. They hoisted the pieces into the tower. Ulysses quickly put the pieces together again.

"All right, boys. Let 'er rip!" Ulysses cried.

The little cannon boomed. Shells rained on the rooftops. The Mexican snipers fled.

"All right, boys. Let 'er rip!" Ulysses cried

"Come on, boys!" said Ulysses. "That did it. We can escape now."

The Americans were capturing the outposts and pressing nearer to Mexico City. Ulysses' regiment was ordered to attack a Mexican trench on a hillside. The men scrambled up the hill and into the trench. They fought fiercely with the Mexicans and soon the Mexicans were retreating.

Ulysses saw an American soldier lying, face down, in a trench. Ulysses bent over him.

"Why, it's Fred Dent!" he exclaimed in amazement. "He's not dead! He's breathing."

Then Ulysses saw a Mexican soldier aiming his rifle straight at Fred's head. Ulysses sprang out of the trench. He knocked the rifle from the Mexican's hand. Before he could pick up the rifle, the Mexican had slipped away through the bushes.

Ulysses carried Fred to a place of safety.

"You've been wounded, Fred," Ulysses said, as Fred opened his eyes. "But not very badly. You're going to get well."

Fred grinned feebly and muttered: "Good

old Sam Grant! Always knows just what to do. Always cool as a cucumber."

The Americans continued to advance. In September, 1847, they captured Mexico City.

Led by General Scott, they entered the city in triumph.

Lieutenant Ulysses S. Grant was promoted because of his courage in action. Before very long, young Captain Grant was hurrying to Missouri to marry Miss Julia Dent.

CHAPTER ELEVEN

The Torchlight Parade

IT WAS a warm afternoon in November, 1860. Ulysses Grant stood at the open door of a store in Galena, Illinois. He was no longer wearing a uniform. The clothes he wore were those of a businessman. Above his head, on the store front, was a sign which read: *Harness and Leather Goods*. The store belonged to Mr. Jesse Grant, and Ulysses was the manager of it.

Ulysses Grant had never wanted to be a soldier. He had never liked army life, especially in peace times. Several years before, he had told Julia, his wife, that he intended to resign from the Army.

"I'm tired of being sent from one post to another," he had said. "I'd rather be a civilian with a business of my own."

Julia had agreed. She did not like army life, either.

"I'll be glad to settle down in a quiet town

somewhere," she said. "That will be better for our children, too. They can have a happy childhood, going to school and making friends whom they can keep always."

"Of course, if my country should ever need me, I would return to the Army at once, Julia." Ulysses said. "If there should be a war, I would immediately volunteer my services."

"Oh, yes, of course!" said Julia.

When Ulysses left the Army, he had thought that he could easily change himself from a soldier into a businessman. But he had not been very successful at anything he tried to do. Finally his father had offered him the position in the Galena store.

"Lyss," Jesse Grant had said, "selling leather is an honest, profitable trade. I've prospered at it. I have tanneries and stores in Ohio, and I've started a business in Galena, Illinois. Why don't you go to work there?"

So Ulysses had thanked his father and come to Galena.

"And how comfortable we are here," Julia often said, "in our nice white cottage, with a big yard for the children to play in!"

[*118*]

"How comfortable we are here," Julia often said

Now Ulysses was smiling, as he watched his son Frederick running down the street toward him.

"Hello, Frederick!" he called. "What's your hurry?"

Frederick was ten. He had brown hair and blue eyes like his father's.

"I thought maybe you'd close the store early because it's Election Day," Frederick said. "I thought maybe I'd walk home with you, and we could see all the people going in and out of the voting place."

"A good idea," Ulysses said. "Just wait a jiffy until I lock up."

Frederick was much interested in the election. He pulled his father along toward the voting place. When they reached the building, he stared at the sober-faced men who were gathered outside.

"Oh, Papa," he said, "there's my schoolmaster, Mr. Wilson. I want you to meet him."

"I'd like to," Ulysses replied.

Frederick introduced his father to the schoolmaster.

"Why haven't we met before, Mr. Grant?" asked Mr. Wilson, as they shook hands.

"Well, sir, I've been living in Galena only a few months," Ulysses said. "Not quite long enough to vote today."

"Did you vote for Abraham Lincoln, Mr. Wilson?" asked Frederick.

"Frederick!" Ulysses exclaimed. "You mustn't ask such questions."

Mr. Wilson smiled. "Don't scold the boy, Mr. Grant. I make no secret of my admiration for Abraham Lincoln. I hope that he'll be elected as our President."

"I hope so, too," Ulysses said, "even though the Southern states secede."

"Secede?" Frederick repeated curiously. "What does that mean?"

"It means to withdraw from the Union," Ulysses explained. "Lincoln is a Northerner. The Southern states fear that, as President, he might make laws against slavery. They have threatened to secede and form a separate country, if Lincoln is elected."

"But can they do it, Papa?"

"Not according to our Constitution," Ulysses said. "The Constitution binds all the states together in a Union. Most Northerners believe that no state or group of states should be allowed to withdraw from the Union. They believe that to secede is wrong."

"Suppose the Southern states secede anyway?" Frederick asked. "What will happen then?"

"The other states will have to act to bring the seceding states back into the Union, Frederick," said Mr. Wilson. "And it may take a war to bring them back."

Frederick thought about this. "Then Papa will be a soldier again."

"Again?" Mr. Wilson looked at Ulysses. "Were you once a soldier?"

"Yes, sir," Ulysses said. "I was a soldier for fifteen years."

"Papa went to West Point," Frederick said proudly. "He was an officer, a captain."

"Indeed!" Mr. Wilson exclaimed. "I didn't know that, Mr. Grant."

"Oh, Papa never tells anybody," said Frederick. "Mr. Wilson, when will we find out whether Abraham Lincoln is elected?"

"Probably not until tomorrow," Mr. Wilson replied. "The votes will have to be counted. Millions of votes. But by tomorrow night, the telegraph wires should be flashing the news."

The next day was an anxious one for Frederick. Ulysses understood his son's feelings. At suppertime the results of the election still were not known.

"Frederick," Ulysses said, "you may stay up with your mother and me, after the younger children go to bed. Perhaps we'll hear something."

It was late and Frederick was getting very sleepy when a sudden noise sounded in the street. Frederick hopped out of his chair and ran to the window.

"Papa! Mama!" he cried. "A parade! A torchlight parade!"

Frederick raced to the front door and out onto the porch. His father and mother followed him. They saw a long line of men

[*123*]

rounding the corner. The men were blowing horns and waving brightly flaring torches. And they were shouting:

"Lincoln! Abraham Lincoln of Illinois!"

Ulysses put his hand on Frederick's shoulder. "Lincoln has been elected," he said.

"Oh, good!" exclaimed Frederick. And he shouted at the top of his voice: "Abraham Lincoln of Illinois!"

The parading men flourished their torches. They whooped and yelled. The whole street seemed to be filled with light and motion.

When the last of the parade had passed, the Grants went into the house.

"It was chilly out there," Julia said. "Sit by the fire, my dears, and I'll make you both a cup of hot chocolate."

As his mother went to the kitchen, Frederick asked, "Will there be a war now, Papa?"

"I hope not," answered his father gravely. "I hope and pray that war may be avoided. But perhaps it can't be. The next few months will tell."

CHAPTER TWELVE

"Duty, Honor, Country!"

SOON after Abraham Lincoln's election as President, seven Southern states seceded from the Union. They named themselves the Confederate States of America. They formed a government and set about raising an army. When Lincoln had been President just thirty-nine days, Confederate cannon bombarded United States troops in Fort Sumter, South Carolina.

The date was April 12, 1861. It marked the beginning of a terrible war.

People in the North, the East, and the West were shocked.

"The Union must be saved!" they declared.

President Lincoln sent out a call for seventy-five thousand volunteers who would fight to save the Union. In all the cities and villages, on all the farms and ranches, men hastened to enlist.

In Galena, Illinois, Ulysses S. Grant immediately gave up his business as a leather merchant. He wrote to the War Department in Washington, saying that he wanted to fight for his country.

"You'll surely receive an officer's commission, Ulysses," Julia said.

"You'll be made a high-ranking officer, Papa," Frederick added.

"Oh, it doesn't matter what my rank is," said his father. "I only want to know how I can help!"

"I guess you'll hear from Washington right away," said Frederick.

"Yes, I think so," Ulysses said.

But several weeks went by, and he heard nothing.

The people of Galena held a big patriotic meeting. They decided that the town ought to send a company of volunteers to the Army.

"We have enough men for a company," they said.

Mr. Wilson, the schoolmaster, got up in the meeting.

"We have someone who is able to train the volunteers, too," he said. "Mr. Grant has been a soldier, a captain. He can teach the Galena men their duties."

Ulysses was quite willing to train the Galena volunteers.

"It's something to do," he told Julia. "It's being useful."

He drilled the men in a vacant lot at the edge of town. He was very strict, but the men liked and respected him. Sometimes they talked about him among themselves. They said that he deserved a better command than this. They wondered why he wasn't leading a company of seasoned troops instead of drilling raw recruits.

Every evening Frederick came out to the lot to walk home with his father. Every evening Ulysses Grant asked the same question.

"Any word from Washington?"

"No, Papa," Frederick always replied. "Not yet."

One evening Frederick said angrily: "Those silly folks in Washington! Don't they want you, Papa? Don't they know what a fine, brave soldier you are?"

[*128*]

"We must be patient, my boy."

"But, Papa, you've *been* patient!"

"Even if I got a commission, I wouldn't have the money to buy a uniform, Frederick."

"Oh, Papa, what a shame it is!" Frederick exclaimed. "I feel so sorry for you."

The Galena men finished their training and went off to join an Illinois regiment. Then a second company of volunteers was organized to drill in the vacant lot, and Ulysses took charge of it. He was still waiting for his commission. He was puzzled and restless, but he never lost his temper.

"I may get a letter by the next mail," he thought.

How he wished and hoped for that letter!

"Soon I'll be the only able-bodied man left in Galena. People will think I'm a coward!" he said to himself.

At the end of a hot summer day, Frederick came to the vacant lot as usual.

"Any word from Washington?" Ulysses asked.

"No, sir. Not yet."

At dusk they trudged home and saw Julia standing on the porch. Julia had a yellow envelope in her hand. She was smiling.

"Ulysses!" she cried. "A telegram!"

Ulysses ran pell-mell. With trembling fingers he tore open the envelope.

"Julia! Frederick!" he exclaimed joyfully. "It's a commission! I've been made the colonel of a regiment."

"Well, it's about time!" said Julia, tossing her head.

Frederick was dancing a jig, hopping up and down. "Yip-pee!" he shrieked. "Colonel Grant. *Colonel Grant!*"

Ulysses took command of his regiment at Springfield, the capital city of Illinois. Julia and his four children went with him. It was a very great occasion. Many grand speeches were made that day. But Ulysses Grant did not make a speech. When he was escorted to the platform, he saluted the soldiers and then said calmly and gently:

"Men, go to your quarters."

Frederick had been wandering through the crowd of people who had come to bid the regiment good-by.

"I heard one person say that you don't look much like a colonel, Papa," Frederick said later.

Grant chuckled and glanced down at his shabby suit. "I suppose I don't look at all like a colonel!" he exclaimed.

"I think everybody expected you to talk more," Julia said.

"I couldn't," Ulysses replied. "There were

those hundreds of young men and boys. They were laughing and joking and flinging their hats in the air. They seemed to feel that war is a picnic. How little they know about its

hardships! I was thinking that some of them will be killed and many will be wounded. I love them and I pity them. But I couldn't tell them that. I just couldn't say anything more."

Soon it was time for Julia and the children to leave for New Jersey, where they were going to live while Ulysses was in the Army.

"Papa, let me come to visit you at your camp," Frederick begged, as he climbed aboard the train. "Please do!"

"Well, we'll see," his father replied. "Remember, Frederick, you're the man of the family now. I'm depending on you to take good care of your mother and the small fry!"

CHAPTER THIRTEEN

The Western Forts

In FEBRUARY, 1862, Ulysses Grant wrote to his wife:

"I am a brigadier general now, but not because of my accomplishments. President Lincoln was promoting a batch of colonels. I merely happened to be one of the batch. And I still can't afford to buy a uniform."

By this time eleven Southern states had seceded from the Union. Both the North and the South were grimly preparing for a long war. The military leaders of the North had divided their forces into two armies.

They planned that one army should protect Washington, the United States capital. It should also attack the Confederate regiments in Virginia. The other army would try to gain control of the Mississippi River, clear to the Gulf of Mexico.

Ulysses S. Grant was with this second, or western, army. He had his headquarters at Cairo, Illinois, which was close to Kentucky. There he was studying maps and charts.

"A military problem is like an arithmetic problem," he thought. "And I've never seen an arithmetic problem that couldn't be solved!"

General Grant fought his first battle against the Confederate troops who had swarmed into Kentucky. Grant won it. The battle was not big or important. But Grant had something very important in mind.

A fleet of seven gunboats was stationed in the Mississippi River near Cairo. Commodore Foote of the United States Navy commanded the fleet.

Grant consulted with Commodore Foote.

"The Confederates are occupying a string of forts on the Tennessee and Cumberland Rivers," he told the Navy officer. "These forts should be ours. I plan to capture them."

"It is a daring plan, General," said Commodore Foote.

"Will your gunboats aid me?"

"They will," said Commodore Foote. "Lead on! I like a scrap."

The rain was pouring in torrents and the roads were flooded, as Grant's men started for Fort Heiman on the Tennessee River. The regiments waded through ankle-deep water and mud.

And when they reached Fort Heiman, the Confederates were not there.

"They were warned of our coming," Grant said. "They must have retreated to Fort Henry. We'll catch them in Fort Henry."

Rain continued to fall. The flood was rising. The soldiers pushed slowly onward. Commodore Foote's gunboats could travel faster. The gunboats arrived first at Fort Henry and bombarded it.

"I shelled the fort," Commodore Foote announced to General Grant, later that day. "I peppered it with fire. In a half hour, the Confederates hauled down their flag and scooted to Fort Donelson on the Cumberland River."

"Is that where they are now?" Grant asked.

"Yes, twenty-one thousand of them. They've dug themselves in. And they have plenty of food and ammunition. Donelson will be a hard nut to crack, General."

"We will crack it," said Grant.

He had seventeen thousand men. The rain had changed to sleet and snow. To make the marching easier, the men threw away their soaking wet blankets and their heavy overcoats. They could not build campfires, for fear of being seen by enemy spies. But they did not halt until they were within sight of Fort Donelson.

The gunboats were ready and waiting. Grant consulted again with Foote.

"I'll bottle up the Confederates on the land side, so that they can't retreat farther," he told the commodore. "You hit them with all your might from the river. Watch for my signal."

"We'll be watching," said Foote. "It should be a lovely scrap!"

At three o'clock in the afternoon Grant signaled. The gunboats blasted from the river.

But the cannon in the fort roared defiantly. Confederate shells raked Foote's vessels.

"They've got the range on Foote," Grant muttered. "Those shells are blasting holes in his boats."

Then he saw that the boats were in danger

of sinking. He saw them swing around and sail off, one by one, up the river.

Night closed in. It was cold and foggy. The soldiers shivered in the darkness. At dawn a messenger from Commodore Foote came looking for Grant. Foote had been wounded.

"He wants to talk with you, sir, and he's too weak to leave the flagship," said the messenger.

Grant mounted a horse. He rode to the spot where the fleet was anchored. A skiff took him out to the flagship.

Foote was lying on a couch in his cabin. He had a bloody bandage on his head. But he was smiling.

"Well, General," he said, "you see what they've done to us? The boys in gray were tougher than I thought. My beautiful boats will have to be mended before we go on with our scrap. I don't imagine that you want to call it all off and turn back?"

"No, Commodore," Grant said. "I never turn back."

"Nor do I! But what's your plan now?"

"I'll keep the enemy bottled up until your boats are repaired."

"Very good, General," said Foote, saluting.

Grant got into the skiff again. Two sailors were at the oars. As they pulled to the shore and Grant stepped out, the sailors looked after him.

"Who's the little guy with the whiskers, Hank?" said one sailor to his companion.

"Why, he's the general," Hank said. "He bosses the whole shebang."

"Him a general? Well, you'd never know it!"

"His men know it, all right," said Hank wisely. "They'll tell you how he's always cool and soft-spoken, but not afeared to tackle a buzz saw."

Grant had left his horse on the shore, tied to a tree. He was just untying the horse when a Union officer darted toward him.

"General Grant!"

"Yes?" Grant said calmly.

The officer was panting and frightened. "Sir, an attack!" he gasped. "The Confederates are ripping through our line!"

Grant leaped into the saddle and rode furiously back to the Union line. He saw that in one place the line had been broken and several of his regiments were retreating from a swarm of gray-clad Confederates.

"But most of the line is holding fast!" he cried. "This is not an attack! Those graycoats

[*141*]

know that we've trapped them. They're not attacking! They're trying to *escape!*"

He galloped into the midst of the confusion. He stood up in his stirrups and shouted to his men:

"Don't let them escape! Stop them! Stiffen the line! Drive them back! *Load, aim, fire!*"

When the men heard his voice, they were filled with fresh courage. They obeyed his commands. Their rifles barked sharply again and again. The guns boomed and the Union regiments began to move forward, driving the Confederates back toward the fort, closing in upon them and cutting off their escape.

In a few hours, the Confederate commander in Fort Donelson sent out a messenger, carrying a white flag of truce. The messenger had a note for General Grant.

"The enemy has asked me to state my terms of surrender," Grant said to one of his officers when he had read the note.

He scribbled an answer. "No terms except unconditional and immediate surrender can be accepted," he wrote. Then he handed his reply to the messenger, who galloped back to the fort.

Before long the white flag of surrender was flying above Fort Donelson and nearly fifteen thousand weary Southern soldiers had laid down their arms.

General Grant had scored a great victory for the North!

CHAPTER FOURTEEN

Marching South

THE people of the Northern states were delighted to hear that the forts on the Tennessee and Cumberland Rivers had been captured. It was the first big battle which Union troops had won in the war. But not many people knew anything about General Grant.

"Who *is* he?" they asked. "Who is this splendid officer?"

In a little while the newspapers were printing stories about him. The stories said that Grant was a slender, brown-bearded man, not very tall, with very quiet manners. He had at last managed to buy a proper uniform, but he didn't often wear it.

He rode his horse through the rain or tramped through the swamps with his soldiers. He slept on the frozen ground, or under a tree, or in the branches of the tree, if that was more convenient. At West Point he had been nicknamed United States Grant and Uncle Sam Grant, because of his initials.

Now he was to have a new nickname. He was to be called *Unconditional Surrender* Grant.

Grant himself did not even bother to read the stories in the papers. President Lincoln had promoted him to the rank of major general. And he was marching south.

"We must win more than one battle to win the war," he said.

In the spring of that year, Grant's army won another big victory at Shiloh, Tennessee. Grant was helped by the Navy gunboats and by other Union generals. In the autumn he defeated the Confederates at Corinth, Mississippi. Then he went on marching south to Vicksburg, on the Mississippi River. The United States Navy had taken the port of New

Orleans. The Navy's ships were patrolling the Gulf of Mexico. If Vicksburg could be captured, the entire length of the Mississippi would be in the hands of the North.

The Confederates did not intend to let Grant take Vicksburg. They knew how important the city was to them. When Grant reached Vicksburg, he found that it was defended by thousands of Southern troops. All the small towns near it were defended, too. Grant made several attempts to force his way through the Confederate lines, but he and his men were thrown back. Then Grant spread out his huge army around all the towns.

"We have made a circle," he said to the members of his staff. "Vicksburg is the center of the circle. We have cut off Vicksburg's sources of supplies. Now we'll wait. The Confederate troops inside this circle will either have to fight us in a pitched battle or starve."

One spring day Grant told his officers that his son Frederick was coming to the camp.

"For months Frederick has been begging for a visit with me," he said. "This seems a good time for it."

The officers were astonished. "Isn't it risky for a boy of twelve to come to an army camp in war times?" they said.

"Yes," Grant replied. "But think of the many, many boys not much older who are risking their lives in this dreadful war. Frederick wants to go to West Point. He wants to be a soldier. I must show him what soldiering really is. It is not all parades and flag-waving and glory."

"Did you want to be a soldier when you were Frederick's age?" the officers inquired.

"No, never," Grant said, smiling. "I seem to be a soldier in spite of myself."

The next day Frederick came. He hugged his father.

"I've had a tent fixed up for you," Grant said. "And I have a pony for you to ride."

"Oh, thanks, Papa!" Frederick's eyes were shining. "Let's go exploring!"

They went together all over the huge camp. They went through the hospital tents and the field kitchens. They clambered in and out of the trenches. Frederick saw the rifle pits and the ammunition dumps.

They went together all over the huge camp

"How did you move so much stuff down here, Papa?" Frederick asked.

"Well, it was slow and difficult," Grant said. "Roads and bridges had to be built. The men had to be fed and the sick cared for. Southern raiders were constantly pestering us. We had bloody skirmishes with them on the way."

"It must have been a terrible job, Papa."

"Yes, but I didn't do it alone," Grant said. "I had lots of fine people working with me. And I don't win these battles alone, either, Frederick. Most of the credit belongs to my men and my staff of officers."

"Oh, Papa! Other generals have good men and officers, and they don't win their battles."

"Maybe I'm luckier than the other generals," Grant said.

"And maybe you're smarter," said his son.

Frederick stayed in the camp for several weeks. He would have liked to stay forever. He was a great favorite with the soldiers. They gave him an army cap to wear, and a cartridge belt and a rifle and a canteen. He ate his meals with the soldiers and slept on an army cot in his own tent.

But Grant was making plans for a big attack on Vicksburg. He had waited long enough.

"I'm going to pack you off to your mother," he told Frederick.

"Oh, shucks!" Frederick exclaimed. "If you win this battle, will it be the end of the war?"

"No, indeed," Grant said. "But it will split the Confederacy in two. It will give our eastern army a better chance in Virginia. You know, my men are only a part of the millions of men who are fighting in this war."

"Yes, I know," Frederick said. "But, Papa, the war will end sometime. And we'll win it, won't we?"

"I think so." Grant nodded. "Put your things in your satchel, son. I'll have to send you home."

Frederick looked gloomy as he put his things into his satchel. "When may I visit you again?" he asked.

"Later, perhaps," Grant said. "We'll see."

In the early summer, Grant prepared to strike with all his power at Vicksburg. He attacked the Confederate defenses and took them, one by one. The Confederate troops fought hard, but they were no match for Grant's army. On July 4, 1863, Grant marched into Vicksburg.

The capture of Vicksburg was a great victory. And on the same day Union troops were winning another great victory in a battle at Gettysburg in Pennsylvania. The news of these victories traveled quickly throughout the country.

The people of the North were glad to receive the news.

"Now," they said, "there is a chance that the Union will be saved."

[151]

CHAPTER FIFTEEN

"Never Turn Back!"

THE train steamed into the Washington station.

Among the passengers who alighted were a soldier and a slim young boy.

It was a mild afternoon in March, 1864. The station was crowded. Newspaper reporters were in the crowd; for it had been said that the famous General Grant was coming to see President Lincoln today.

But nobody paid any attention to the soldier in the old hat and faded blue uniform. Nobody noticed him or the boy, as they walked to the street and got into a horse-drawn cab.

"Are we going right to the White House?" the boy said.

"Yes, Frederick. I don't want a lot of fool-ishness and fancy business about this."

Frederick was excited. He wouldn't have minded the foolishness and fancy business. What other boy had a father who was the hero of the nation?

"Wasn't George Washington the first Amer-ican to be made Lieutenant General of all the United States Armies, Papa? And aren't you the only man ever to be made Lieutenant General since then?"

"Yes," Grant said. "Congress passed a bill reviving the rank. The President had to give the commission to someone. I suppose he couldn't think of anyone else."

"Oh, Papa!" Frederick said. "Everybody knows that Congress passed the bill just for you."

The cab rolled into the driveway of the White House.

"Look at the carriages," Grant said. "Presi-dent Lincoln must be having a reception. Well, I won't go in."

But he had to go in, for a servant was opening the cab door.

Grant entered the White House and went

down the hall toward a big parlor. Frederick
followed him. The parlor was filled with people and the hum of conversation.

"Frederick, I'm not going in there," Grant said, stopping in the doorway. "I can't."

But the people had seen him. They stopped talking. They drew aside, and President Lincoln strode forward to clasp his hand.

"I'm glad to see you, General," Lincoln said heartily.

"It's Grant!" the people exclaimed. "General Grant!"

They surged around him. They lifted him to a sofa, so that they could have a better view of him. He was red-faced and embarrassed.

Mrs. Lincoln took pity on him.

"Walk around the parlor with me, General," she said, when he had stepped down from the sofa. Then she whispered: "You can get away through this side hall, if you wish."

Grant got away. He and Frederick hurried to a hotel.

The clerk at the hotel desk peered at the poorly dressed soldier and said: "The only room I have is a little one up in the attic."

"That will do," Grant replied. He wrote his name in the hotel register.

"What!" the clerk gasped. "Are you Ulysses

S. *Grant?* Oh, excuse me, sir. Yes, yes, General Grant, I have an elegant room for you!"

"No," Grant said. "Just put us in the little one."

When they were in their room, Frederick laughed. "This is fun, Papa."

"Fun? It's awful!" Grant wiped beads of sweat from his brow. "The President said that I'm to be formally presented with the commission tomorrow. And I hope it'll be done without more foolishness!"

The next day he was made Lieutenant General of all the Armies. No man but George Washington had ever been so honored.

After the ceremony he rode out in a carriage to inspect the troops who were guarding the city. It was raining, but great throngs greeted him everywhere.

"Hurrah for Grant!" they shouted. "We've got a *real* general at last!"

Grant was going to command the Army of the Potomac now. He planned to capture Richmond, Virginia. This city was the capital of the Confederacy.

"To take Richmond, I'll have to defeat Robert E. Lee's forces in Virginia," Grant said to Frederick. "It will mean terrific fighting. Lee is a fine commander. He was a hero in the Mexican War. He was the most brilliant student ever to attend West Point. But this war must end, Frederick. I want *peace*."

"Does Lee want peace, too?" said Frederick.

"I'm sure he does," Grant said. "But he wants to win. And he knows that if he loses Richmond, he loses everything. So he will fight very bravely."

When Frederick had once more been "packed off," Grant went into Virginia. Soon his blue-clad regiments were marching to the south. They had not gone far before they found Lee's troops.

The two armies clashed in a region known as the Wilderness. It was a desolate country, covered with scrubby trees and brush. Fierce battles were fought. The flash of the guns set the woods on fire. The soldiers struggled through clouds of smoke and flame. In two days, seventeen thousand of Grant's men died.

Grant grieved for the dead. He worried about the wounded. But he had started for Richmond, and he would not stop.

"The enemy is retreating," he said. "I purpose to fight it out on this line, if it takes all summer."

Mile by mile, the Union regiments advanced.

Grant was cool and determined and fearless.

"The Old Man ain't one to peek through a spyglass at the shooting," said his soldiers. "Oh, no! He's always right in it, up to his neck. Reckon he can't count the bullets he's dodged. And many's the horse that's been shot out from under him. Oh, he's a daisy! A hunky-dory daisy!"

The summer dragged by. It was autumn, then winter, and the weather was very bad. Grant had circled around through Virginia, so that he could approach Richmond from the south. He was at a place called City Point.

"Nothing can be done in such weather. We'll rest here," he decided.

During the winter President Lincoln him-

Mile by mile, the Union regiments advanced

self came to City Point to confer with Grant. Lincoln rode horseback through the camp, inspecting it. And what an odd figure he was, in the saddle! He sat hunched up, his high black hat bouncing over his eyes, the tails of his rusty black coat fluttering in the wind, his long legs dangling.

The soldiers grinned to see him. "Don't he look like a scarecrow?" they said. But they loved him. "He's our Old Honest Abe," they said.

In the spring, Grant moved again toward Richmond. He took the town of Petersburg. This had been the Confederates' stronghold. It protected their capital. They had fought desperately to keep it.

"Now we can't fail to capture Richmond," Grant said to his men when Petersburg fell. "We have just twenty miles to go. March on!"

On the morning of April 3, his army smashed through the last fortifications and entered Richmond. But this time Grant was not leading the march. He had stayed a little in the rear. He felt sorry for the people in the city. He felt sorry for the Southern soldiers and did not want to see them so badly beaten. Presently a messenger dashed back to him.

"Lee has slipped out, sir," the messenger said. "He is retreating with his army to the Appomattox River."

Grant sighed. "I wish General Lee had not attempted this retreat," he said. "He can gain nothing by it. His men are ragged, hungry, tired. They can't possibly go far. Our regiments are surrounding them. I wish they would surrender before more of them are killed by our guns. But, instead, I must chase after them until they do surrender."

On April 7, Grant was in the village of Farmville, Virginia. At five o'clock in the evening he sent a letter to General Lee.

"The results of the last week," he wrote, "must convince you of the hopelessness of further resistance."

It was a warm, beautiful evening, with spring in the breeze. After he had sent the letter off to Lee, Grant paced up and down the porch of the Farmville tavern. He had a blinding headache. For several days he had been ill. But he had kept on leading his men.

He saw a column of them now, filing past the tavern in the twilight.

And the soldiers saw him.

"There's the Old Man!" somebody cried. "Let's give him a song!"

They kindled bonfires of straw and pine knots in the street in front of the tavern. And as they marched past, they sang rousing songs.

Grant smiled and saluted. But his eyes were wet with tears.

When Lee's answer came, the next day, Grant read it eagerly.

Lee had written: "I shall be pleased to meet you at ten A.M. tomorrow on the old stage road to Richmond, between the picket lines of the two armies."

On the morning of April ninth, Grant and his staff officers went to meet Lee. On the road they were met by an orderly. He showed them the way to the house of Major McLean. The major had offered his house for the meeting place of the two generals.

As they entered the parlor, they saw General Lee standing there, very straight and tall. Grant and Lee shook hands.

Grant was wearing a private's uniform. His trousers were tucked into the cuffs of his mud-splashed boots. He had no spurs or sword or sash. Lee was dressed in a brand-new uniform. His boots were polished. His spurs glistened.

His sash was of fringed silk. From his belt hung a gold sword with a jeweled hilt and scabbard.

The two generals sat down at a table, facing each other.

Grant looked at Lee and thought: "He is a brave and gallant soldier. I respect and honor him. I must be very kind to him."

After a little pause, Grant spoke in low, gentle tones. "I know how hard this is for you, sir. I shall offer you fair terms. The firing on both sides must cease immediately." He glanced at Lee's sparkling sword and added: "The Southern officers may keep their weapons, their horses, and baggage."

Lee nodded his handsome gray head, as if in gratitude.

"Your regiments must disband," Grant said. "Any of your enlisted men who own horses or mules may take the animals home with them. They will be needed for the spring plowing and planting of crops on Southern farms."

"Of course, we have no ammunition to turn over to you, sir," Lee said. "And no food.

Grant and Lee shook hands

My army has been without rations for days."

"Your army will be fed, sir." Grant motioned to one of his officers. "See that 25,000 rations are given to the Confederate troops without delay," he ordered.

Further arrangements for the surrender were made. At last Lee got to his feet. He shook hands again with Grant. He bowed to the members of Grant's staff. Then he walked out of the house and down the porch steps.

Grant walked behind him. As Lee mounted his horse, Grant stood watching, his hat in his hand.

Lee raised his broad-brimmed gray hat to Grant and rode slowly, sadly away.

When the weary Union soldiers heard that Lee had surrendered, they yelled and shot their guns into the air. But Grant sternly silenced them.

"Rejoice that peace has come to our beloved country," he said. "Rejoice that the Southerners are our countrymen again. But do so *quietly*."

CHAPTER SIXTEEN

Joy and Sorrow

GRANT walked out of the Washington hotel and started toward the White House. It was April 14. The city was gay with banners and bunting. Bands were playing in the streets. People were laughing and singing and dancing. Everybody was wildly happy because the cruel war was over.

Suddenly someone cried: "Look, there's Grant!"

Then the people swooped around him. The admiring mob hemmed him in. He could not take a single step. He could scarcely breathe. If policemen hadn't rushed to rescue him, he might have been smothered.

At the White House, President Lincoln welcomed him with open arms. They talked about the future. The Union had been saved. But much work was still to be done. Lincoln had said that he would strive for a just and lasting peace. Many thousands of soldiers had been killed. Their widows and orphans must be cared for. The South had been almost destroyed. It must be rebuilt. The United States must be made whole again.

Grant pledged himself to help Abraham Lincoln with all these things.

"I hear that Mrs. Grant is here in Washington, too," Lincoln said. "My wife and I are going to the theater tonight. Won't you go with us?"

"Thank you, Mr. President," Grant replied. "But we want to catch the afternoon train for Burlington, New Jersey, where our children are staying."

"Can't you postpone your departure, General?"

Grant took a note from his pocket. "This is from Mrs. Grant. She is reminding me not to miss the train for Burlington. The children are expecting us."

Lincoln smiled. "Then you must *not* miss the train," he said.

Julia Grant had been waiting at the hotel for her husband. When Grant returned, she said nervously: "Ulysses, a strange man has been lurking in the hall outside our door. He stared at me. I was quite frightened."

"Describe the man," Grant told her.

"Well, he was tall and black-haired. He had on a dark cape."

"He's not here now, Julia," Grant said. "Come, we'll drive to the station."

A special car had been reserved for the Grants on the train for Burlington. Sentries guarded it.

"Sir," said one of the sentries, "we found an ugly-looking chap sneaking into your car this morning. He claimed he was a friend of yours."

"Was he wearing a dark cape?" asked Julia.

"Yes, ma'am."

Julia clutched her husband's arm.

"Oh, Ulysses!" she gasped.

"But don't you fret, ma'am," the sentry said. "We didn't believe him. We snatched him out and sent him kiting. He'll not disturb you any."

In the night, as the train sped toward Burlington, Grant received a telegram. He read it and his face paled.

"Julia!" he cried. "President Lincoln is dying!"

"What!" Julia exclaimed.

"He was at Ford's Theater. A madman named John Wilkes Booth shot him. Oh,

[170]

Julia, how terrible!" Grant bowed his head in his hands.

"It was the same man, Ulysses!" Julia said. "The man in the cape. He meant to kill you, too!"

Soon they learned that this was true. John Wilkes Booth was the leader of a group of conspirators. These conspirators were angry because the South had been defeated. They wanted revenge. They had plotted to murder Abraham Lincoln and other Northern statesmen, and Grant, too.

Grant left his wife at Burlington. Then he went back to Washington. The city was hushed in sorrow. Government buildings were draped in black. Flags were at half-mast. The people in the streets were weeping. The nation which had been so happy was plunged into despair.

Grant ordered out squads of soldiers.

"Track down the murderers!" he said. "They must be punished for their crime. Arrest them. They must be tried and hanged for treason."

Soon all of the conspirators except Booth

himself were seized. And a little later news-boys were running everywhere, crying: "Extra! Extra! Booth is dead! Booth is dead!"

Booth had been burned to death in a barn, as he hid from the searching parties.

Andrew Johnson had been the Vice-President of the United States. He became President now. Johnson was a good man. But many Americans felt that no one could fill Lincoln's place. No one else could do the work which Lincoln had left unfinished. They were mournful and frightened.

"General Grant," said President Johnson, "the people of the North have confidence in you. They want to see you, and express their gratitude and affection. They have invited you to tour the Northern states. Do not refuse the invitation. Our citizens will be comforted if you speak to them."

Grant had not forgotten his pledge to Lincoln. "Very well," he said. "I'll go."

He went into New England and into the Middle West. He traveled from city to city and spoke to millions of people.

He went to his old home at Galena

"Be brave and hopeful," he told them. "Have faith in your government and in the future."

He went to his old home at Galena. He also went to Ohio to see his parents and other relatives.

How glad his mother and father were to have him eat dinner at the long family table again!

"It's like old times, Lyss," Jesse Grant declared.

Then President Johnson asked Grant to tour the South also.

Grant hesitated. "I'll go," he said, "though the Southern people may hate me for fighting them."

But the Southerners did not hate him. He had commanded the armies which conquered them. But he had only been doing his duty. And when they were defeated, he had treated them kindly and generously. The Southerners felt that Grant was really their friend. Many of them came to him for advice and encouragement.

President Johnson soon appointed **Grant** to his Cabinet. Grant served as Secretary **of** War until January, 1868.

That was an election year. A new President was to be elected.

Who would be the new President?

One name was most often suggested, **the** name of the most popular man in the country.

CHAPTER SEVENTEEN

The New President

THE early morning of March 4, 1869, was cold and cloudy. But at eleven o'clock, the skies suddenly cleared. The sun shone down brightly on the city of Washington. The streets around the Capitol were crowded with people.

This was Inauguration Day.

Ulysses S. Grant was on his way to be inaugurated as President of the United States. Voters in all parts of the country had elected him.

A great procession was moving slowly toward the Capitol building. Companies of soldiers rode on high-stepping horses. Companies of soldiers marched on foot. Regiments of battle-scarred veterans tramped by, flourishing their stained and tattered banners.

West Point had sent its cadet corps. And one of those trim young cadets was Frederick Dent Grant! Drums rolled. Military bands made music.

Grant was riding in a plain, undecorated carriage. His clothes were dark and plain. He seemed calm and thoughtful.

The procession stopped at the east side of the Capitol. A wide balcony had been erected there. Grant stepped down from his carriage and went into the Capitol. The vast crowd below the balcony waited in silence.

In a few minutes the Justices of the Supreme Court came out on the balcony. They were dressed in their long black gowns. The Chief Justice had a Bible in his hand.

Then Grant appeared on the balcony.

The crowd broke into thundering cheers: "Grant! Hurrah for Grant!"

He stood looking over the sea of upturned faces. He knew that near him, somewhere, were Julia and his children. His parents were there, and his brothers and sisters, and the Marshalls and the Ammens and countless old friends and schoolmates and good comrades.

He knew that all these people were proud of him at this moment.

He prayed that they might always be as proud.

The Chief Justice of the Supreme Court raised his hand from the Bible and spoke the words of the oath.

He stood looking over the sea of upturned faces

Grant laid his own hand on the Bible and repeated the words:

" 'I do solemnly swear that I will faithfully execute the office of President of the United States, and will, to the best of my ability, preserve, protect, and defend the Constitution of the United States.' "

He bent his head and touched the Bible with his lips.

When he straightened up, he was smiling a little.

Perhaps he was thinking of a long-ago night in Georgetown, Ohio, and of what a phrenologist had said about an awkward, blushing, village boy. Perhaps he was remembering how the boy had said in amazement: "But, Papa, I'm not going to be President of the United States!" Perhaps he was smiling at the memory of Jesse Grant rattling a newspaper and answering:

"I guess it could happen, Lyss."

Born April 27, 1822,
at Point Pleasant, Ohio

Enters the United States Military Academy
at West Point, 1839

Receives the rank of captain, for gallantry
in the Mexican War, 1847

Marries Julia Dent, 1848

Dies at Mt. McGregor, New York,
on July 23, 1885

Inaugurated President of the United States, 1869